Spring Harvest Praise 1998

Music Edition

SPRING HARVEST

Equipping the Church for action

Introduction

Spring Harvest's twentieth year sees another Songbook reflecting the depth and diversity of material available to enhance our worship.

It has been said that music is a great servant, but a bad master – a comment that I find easy to endorse. We must avoid moving to an extreme where music can be abused, and I am delighted that Spring Harvest has maintained a balance in this respect. Down through the years, the Event has spawned wonderful worship material - music that has credibility, accompanying words of integrity.

I trust that this current edition continues the process, bringing joy to the worshipper and, supremely, to the One who alone is worthy of our worship. It is a balanced collection of hymns, songs, liturgy and passages for meditation, reflecting various styles and emphases in worship evident at the Event.

The Spring Harvest Executive joins me in wishing you God's blessing as you use this book as a further resource for your ministry.

Dave Pope
on behalf of the **Spring Harvest Executive**

Contents

Index of Bridges

Many of the songs in this book can be found on Spring Harvest albums — available from your local Christian Bookshop or direct from Spring Harvest.

Index

Song titles differing from first lines are in italics

4

5

Index — continued

Song titles differing from first lines are in italics

Index of Liturgy

Index of Prayers

Index of Bible Verses

1 All Good Gifts Around Us
(We Plough The Fields)

Trish Morgan

9

2   All I Once Held Dear
(Knowing You)

Phil 3: 7-11
Graham Kendrick

♩ = 65

1. All I once held dear, built my life up - on, all this world re - veres and
heart's de - sire is to know you— more, to be found in you and
know the power of your ri - sen— life, and to know you in your

wars to own; all I once thought gain I have coun - ted— loss- spent and
known as yours; to pos - sess by faith what I could not— earn - all - sur-
suf - fer - ings; to be - come like you in your death, my— Lord, so with

Chorus

worth- less now, com - pared to this.
pass - ing gift of right - eous - ness.   Know- ing you, Je- sus,
you to live and ne - ver die!

This song is recorded on the Spring Harvest 1994 Live Worship Album and the 1994 New Songs Album.

know-ing you, there is no great - er thing: you're my

all, you're the best,— you're my joy, my right-eous-ness; and I love you, Lord.—

2. Now my
3. O to love you, Lord,— love, you, Lord.—

3   All My Ways

Steve James

1. All my ways,— all our hearts— the ma - kers hand, re-
(2) Spi - rit's work,— o - be - dience won,— you will not rest till

flec - ted in each part. But bro - ken lives have
we re - flect the Son. His bro - ken life re -

shat - tered all of you— that we can see.
stores us in for - give - ness to your side.

Re - store O Lord,— your face in me.— Through
His cross - work done,— the vic - tory won.—

4 All The Earth Will Be Filled

With strength

David Hadden

1. All the earth— will be filled— with the glo-ry of the Lord and the
(2) north and south— and east and west,— men and wo-men all con-fess— to the

know-ledge—— of the Lord God Al-migh-ty.—————— And
lord-ship—— of—— Je-sus their Mes-si-ah.—————— He

ev-ery man— of ev-ery tongue— will see the work that God has done and ack-
is our friend,— he is our King.— A sa-cri-fice— of praise we bring as we ack-

now-ledge—— the glo-ry of the Lord.——— Con-fess-ing Je-sus,
now-ledge—— the glo-ry of the Lord.———

ev - ery knee___ shall bow, con - fess - ing Je - sus,

ev - ery tongue___ de - clare that he is Christ, King, Lord and friend. The

earth will be filled with the glo - ry of the Lord.___ 2. From

(Fine)

D.C. al Fine

4a   Come let us worship!

God in Christ has revealed his glory;
come let us worship.

From the rising of the sun to its setting;
the Lord's name is greatly to be praised.

Give him praise you servants of the Lord;
O praise the name of the Lord!

5 And Can it Be

Words: Charles Wesley
Music: Thomas Campbell's Bouquet
Arr. Chris Norton

1. And can it be that
2. 'Tis mys-tery all! - The
3. He left his Fa - ther's
4. Long my im - pri - soned

I - should— gain an in - terest— in the— Sav - iour's blood?
Im - mor-tal dies, - who can— ex - plore his— strange de - sign?
throne- a - bove - so free, so— in - fi - nite his grace -
spi - rit— lay fast bound— in— sin and— na - ture's night:

Died he for me,— who caused his pain; for me,——— who him—— to
In vain the first-born se - raph tries to sound——— the depths——— of
emp-tied him - self— of all but love, and bled——— for A - dam's
thine eye dif-fused— a quicken-ing ray; I woke——— the dun - geon

death pur - sued?
love di - vine!
help - less race.
flamed with light.

A - maz - ing love!- How_ can_ it_ be____ that
'Tis mer - cy all! - Let_ earth_ a - dore;____ let
'Tis mer - cy all, im - mense_ and_ free;____ for,
My chains fell off, my_ heart_ was_ free;____ I

thou,____ my God,_shouldst die____ for me?
an - gel minds__ in - quire____ no more.
O____ my God,_ it found__ out me.
rose,____ went forth,_ and fol - lowed thee.

A - maz - ing love! How
'Tis mer - cy all! Let
'Tis mer - cy all, im-
My chains fell off, my

can it be that thou, my God, shouldst_ die for me?
earth a - dore; let an - gel minds in - quire no more.
mense and free; for, O my God, it__ found out me.
heart was free; I rose, went forth, and__ fol- lowed thee.

5. No condemnation now I dread;
Jesus, and all in him, is mine!
Alive in him, my living head,
and clothed in righteousness divine,
bold I approach the eternal throne
and claim the crown through Christ my own;
bold I approach the eternal throne
and claim the crown through Christ my own.

17

6 Are We The People
(Last Generation)

Noel & Tricia Richards

With a driving rhythm ♩ = 126

Are we the peo - ple who— will see— God's king-dom come,—

when he is known— in ev - ery na-

- tion?

One thing is cer-

- tain, we— are clo - ser than— be - fore;

keep mov-ing on,— last gen - er - a - tion.

This song is recorded on the Spring Harvest 1997 New Songs Album and the 1997 Praise Mix.

19

7   As For Me And My House

Moderately

Jim Bailey

As for me— and my house, as for me— and my fa-mi-ly,

as for me— and my chil-dren, we will serve the Lord.—

we will serve the Lord.— In this fa-mi-ly— we're gon-na do things

pro-per-ly,— read God's word ev-ery day,— and then we'll

try to pray.— Al-though we get it wrong,— we will still car-ry on,— make Je-sus num-ber one— in this place. In this place we're gon-na say grace.

7a   The Lord of Every Family
from Ephesians 3.

Let us declare our faith in God

We believe in God the Father,
from whom every family in heaven and on earth is named.
We believe in God the Son,
who lives in our hearts through faith, and fills us with his love.
We believe in God the Holy Spirit,
who strengthens us inwardly with power from on high.
We believe in one God; Father, Son and Holy Spirit.
To him be glory in the church and in Christ Jesus
forever and ever. Amen.

8   As Sure As Gold Is Precious
(Revival)

Robin Mark

1. As sure as gold is precious and the honey sweet, so you love this city and you love these streets.
(2) dreamer dreaming in her dead-end job; every driver driving through the rush hour mob.
(3) preacher preaching when the well is dry to the lost soul reaching for a higher high.
(4) man and woman, every old and young; every father's daughter, every mother's son.

23

Bridges — From B♭

To C

To D

To E♭

To F

To G

9 Be Still

David Evans
Arr. Geoff Baker

Flowing ♩ = 85

1. Be still, for the pre-sence of the Lord, the ho-ly One, is here;
2. Be still, for the glo-ry of the Lord is shin-ing all a-round;
3. Be still, for the pow-er of the Lord is mov-ing in this place:

come bow be-fore him now with re-ver-ence and fear:
he burns with ho-ly fire, with splen-dour he is crowned:
he comes to cleanse and heal, to mi-ni-ster his grace-

in him no sin is found - we stand on ho-ly ground.
how awe-some is the sight - our rad-iant king of light!
no work too hard for him. In faith re-ceive from him.

Be still, for the pre-sence of the Lord, the ho-ly One, is here.
Be still, for the glo-ry of the Lord is shin-ing all a-round.
Be still, for the pow-er of the Lord is mov-ing in this place.

10   Be Thou My Vision

Words: Tr. Mary Elizabeth Byrne (1880-1931)
& Eleanor Henrietta Hull (1860-1935)
Music: Ancient Irish melody

Quietly, building with strength

thought in—— the day and—— the—— night,
Fa - ther—— and I thy—— true—— son,
shel - ter,—— and thou my—— high—— tow'r,
on - ly,—— thou first in—— my—— heart,
own heart,—— what - ev - er—— be - fall,

wak - ing—— or sleep - ing,—— thy—— pre - sence—— my
thou in—— me dwel - ling,—— and—— I with—— thee
raise thou—— me hea - ven - wards,—— O—— pow'r of—— my
high King—— of hea - ven,—— my—— trea - sure—— thou
still be—— my vi - sion,—— thou—— ru - ler—— of

light.————
one.————
pow'r.————
art.————
all.————

Bless The Lord

This song is recorded on the Spring Harvest 1998 New Songs Album.

12 Blessing And Honour
(Ancient Of Days)

Gary Sadler & Jamie Harvill

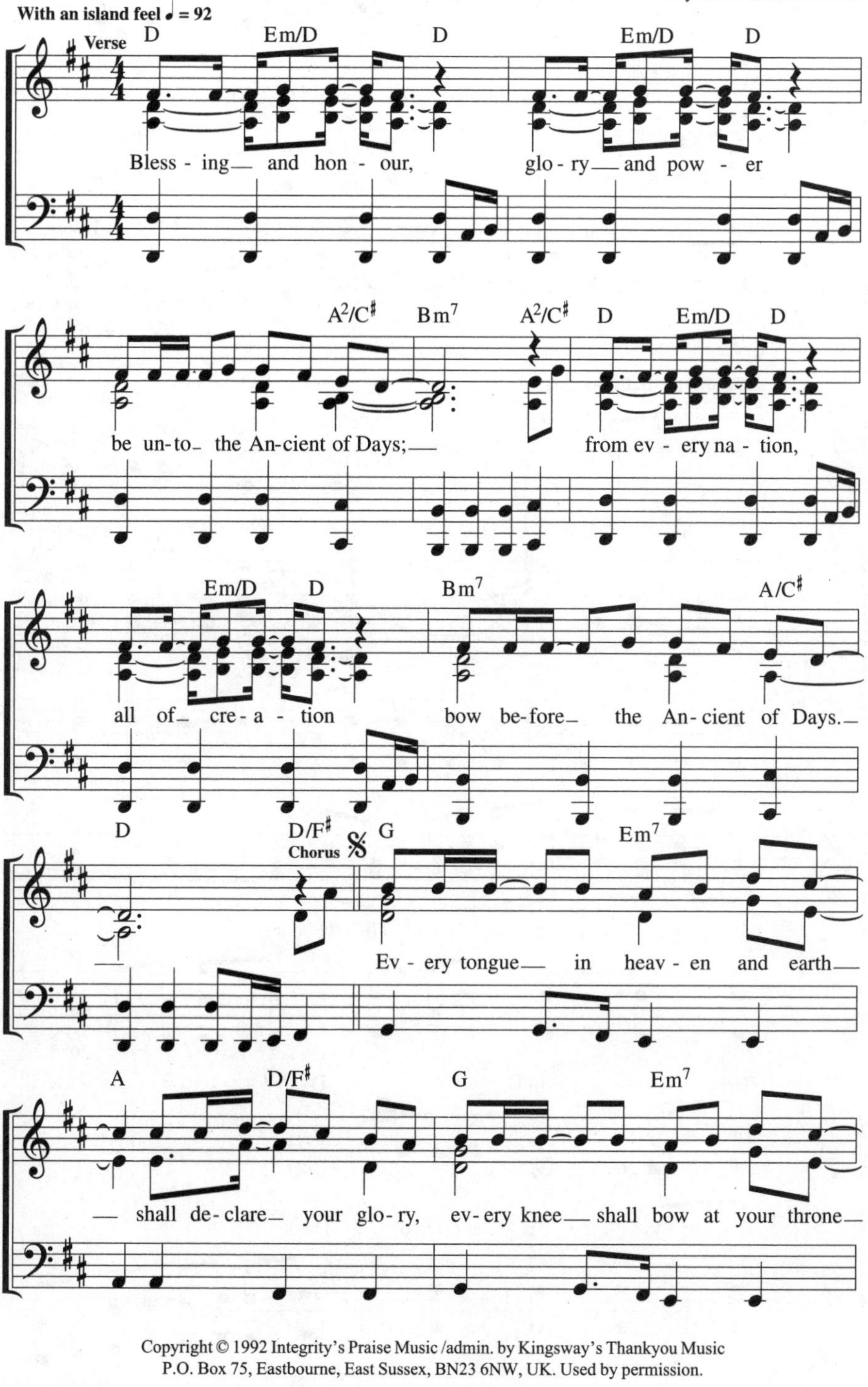

With an island feel ♩ = 92
Verse
D Em/D D Em/D D
Bless - ing and hon - our, glo - ry and pow - er
A2/C# Bm7 A2/C# D Em/D D
be un - to the An - cient of Days; from ev - ery na - tion,
Em/D D Bm7 A/C#
all of cre - a - tion bow be - fore the An - cient of Days.
D D/F# G Em7
Chorus
Ev - ery tongue in heav - en and earth
A D/F# G Em7
shall de - clare your glo - ry, ev - ery knee shall bow at your throne

none can — com-pare to — your match-less worth: _____

sing un-to — the An - cient — of — Days.

O An-cient of Days _____

O An-cient of Days _____

13 Breathe On Me, Breath Of God

Words: Edwin Hatch
in this version Jubilate Hymns
Music: Robert Jackson Arr. Roger Mayor

1. Breathe on me, breath of God: fill me with life a - new, that as you love, so
2. Breathe on me, breath of God, un - til my heart is pure, un - til my will is
3. Breathe on me, breath of God; ful - fil my heart's de - sire, un - til this earth - ly
4. Breathe on me, breath of God; so shall I ne - ver die, but live with you the

This song is recorded on the Spring Harvest 1996 Live Worship Album - Volume 1.

35

14 Broken I Stand
(Kindle The Flame)

Jill Sutheran

Em   Cmaj7   Bm   Em

Bro - ken I stand, mer - cy I need.

Cmaj7   Bm   Em

Stretch out your hand, O Spi - rit lead.

D   C

Fill my heart with the love of God and my mind with all good

G   C   D   Em

things. ___ Bea - con burn - ing turn my

15
By Your Side

Noel & Tricia Richards

By your side I would stay,

in your arms I would lay;

Je-sus, lo-ver of my soul,

no-thing from you I with-hold.

Lord, I love you and a-dore you.
What more can I say? You cause my love to grow strong-er
with ev-ery pass-ing day. day. day.

15a   A Covenant Service

As a company of men and women
who have received Christ as Saviour
and by grace become God's children,
we here and now dedicate ourselves to him;
we desire to renew our commitment
as a church of Jesus Christ,
indwelt by the Holy Spirit
united to walk worthily of our profession,
set apart to proclaim his word,
to observe his commandments,
and by God's grace to work
according to his will for the salvation of others
and for the well-being of his world. **Amen.**

15b   Turning Back to God
from Joel 2 and Revelation 2

Leader   Sisters and brothers, many of us from time to time have
            fallen away from our first love, and have followed other
            lords and served other wills than God's will. Let us then
            remind ourselves of the promises of God in scripture,
            and turn our hearts again to him.

Reader   'Even now,' declares the Lord, 'return to me with all your
            heart, with fasting and weeping and mourning.' Rend
            your heart and not your garments. Return to the Lord
            your God, for he is gracious and compassionate, slow to
            anger and abounding in love.

Leader   Do you now turn your back on every word and action
            which has denied your profession of faith in Christ?
Response   **I turn my back on them.**

Reader   'You have persevered and have endured hardships for
            my name and have not grown weary. Yet this I have
            against you You have forsaken your first love.'

Leader   Do you turn again to the Lord in love and repentance?
Response   **I turn again to him.**

Leader   May almighty God set you free from all that has drawn
            you away from him, & strengthen you to walk
            into his future.
All   **Amen.**

© Mark Earey

15c   Family/relationships
from Colossians 3: 12-14

Therefore, as God's chosen people, holy and dearly loved,
clothe yourselves with compassion, kindness, humility,
gentleness and patience. Bear with each other and forgive
whatever grievances you may have against one another.

Calm Me, O Lord

Jonny Baker & Jon Birch
Arr. R Spencer

Calm me,— O Lord,————
Still me,— O Lord,————

as you still— the storm.—
keep me— from harm.—

Let all the tu-mult with-in me— cease,————

en-fold me, Lord, in your— peace.————

This song is recorded on the Spring Harvest 1998 Praise Mix.

17 Christ Triumphant

Words: Michael Saward
Music: John Barnard

5. Our hearts and voi-ces rais-ing through the a-ges—

1. Christ tri-umph-ant, ev-er reign-ing, Sa-viour, Mas-ter,
2. Word in-car-nate, truth re-veal-ing, Son of Man on
3. Suffer-ing ser-vant, scorned, ill-treat-ed, vic-tim cru-ci-
4. Priest-ly King, en-throned for ev-er high in heaven a-
5. So, our hearts and voi-ces rais-ing through the a-ges

King! Lord of heaven, our lives sus-tain-ing,
earth! Power and ma-jes-ty con-ceal-ing,
fied! Death is through the cross de-feat-ed,
bove! Sin and death and hell shall ne-ver
long, cease-less-ly up-on you gaz-ing,

long, up-on you gaz-ing,

this shall be— our song: yours the glo - ry and the

hear us as we sing:
by your hum - ble birth:
sin - ners jus - ti - fied: yours the glo - ry
sti - fle hymns of love:
this shall be our song:

crown, the high re - nown,———— the e - ter - nal name.

and the crown, the high re - nown, the e - ter - nal name.

17a   The Hope of Glory
from Colossians 1.27

Christ in you, the hope of glory.
This is the gospel we proclaim!

18a   Praising the Lord

from Colossians 1.15-18

You, Christ, are the image of the unseen God,
    the first-born of all creation.
You created all things in heaven and on earth everything
visible and everything invisible, thrones, dominions,
sovereignties, powers all things were created
    through you and for you.

Lord of all creation we worship and adore you.

You are the radiant light of God's glory you hold all
creation together by your word of power.

Lord of all creation we worship and adore you.

You are the first to be born from the dead.
All perfection is found in you,
and all things were reconciled through you and for you,
everything in heaven and everything on earth,
when you made peace by your death on the cross.

Lord of all creation we worship and adore you.

The Church is your body, you are its head.
You take your place in heaven at the right hand
    of the divine majesty,
where we worship and adore you with all your creation,
singing Holy, holy, holy Lord,God of power and might,
heaven and earth are full of your glory.
    Hosanna in the highest.

18b   Following Jesus

Lord Jesus, we will follow you;
Our lives belong to you.
Lord Jesus, we will worship you;
Our hearts belong to you.
Lord Jesus, we will watch and wait for you;
Our futures belong to you.

Lord Jesus, your way is often hard and unappealing;
Help us to persevere until your Kingdom comes.
Lord Jesus, there are other paths that seem so attractive;
Lead us away from all temptation.
Lord Jesus, you stand firm for all that is true and good;
Deliver us from the power of evil.

Lord Jesus, speak clearly to guide us;
and close our ears to all distractions.
Lord Jesus, speak clearly to reassure us;
and close our hearts to all fearful thoughts.
Lord Jesus, speak clearly to challenge us;
and make us single-minded in seeking your Kingdom.

Lord Jesus, your word speaks of your glory
Let us behold it now and always.
Lord Jesus, your word speaks of your grace;
Pour out your love on us we pray.
Lord Jesus, your word speaks of heaven;
Make us ready to live there with you for ever.

19 Come, Let Us All Unite And Sing

Words: Howard Kingsbury c.1850
Music: Old English Air

1. Come, — let us all u - nite and sing - God is love!
2. O — tell the earth's re - mot - est bound - God is love!
3. How — hap - py is our por - rion here - God is love!
4. In — Zi - on we shall sing a - gain - God is love!

God is love! While — heaven and earth their prais - es bring -
God is love! In — Christ is full re - demp - tion found -
God is love! His — pro - mis - es our spi - rits cheer -
God is love! Yes, — this shall be our high - est strain -

God is love! God is love! Let — ev - ery soul from —
God is love! God is love! His — blood can cleanse our —
God is love! God is love! He — is our sun and —
God is love! God is love! Whilst — end - less a - ges —

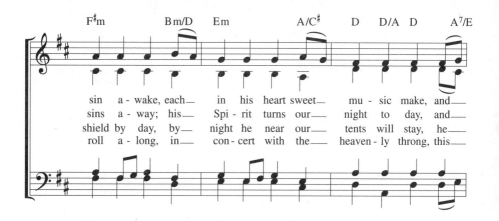

sin a - wake, each— in his heart sweet— mu - sic make, and—
sins a - way; his— Spi- rit turns our— night to day, and—
shield by day, by— night he near our— tents will stay, he—
roll a - long, in— con- cert with the— heaven - ly throng, this—

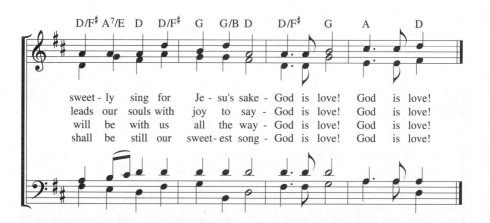

sweet - ly sing for Je - su's sake - God is love! God is love!
leads our souls with joy to say - God is love! God is love!
will be with us all the way - God is love! God is love!
shall be still our sweet- est song - God is love! God is love!

19a United to Christ's Love
from Romans 8

What can separate us from the love of Christ?
Nothing can separate us from the love of Christ!
Can trouble do it?   **No!**
Can hardship do it?   **No!**
Can persecution do it? **No!**
Can hunger do it?   **No!**
Can poverty do it?   **No!**
Can danger do it?   **No!**
Can death do it?   **No!**
So what can separate us from the love of Christ?
Nothing can! Alleluia!

from Scripture Union SALT material

20 Come Let Us Sing Of A Wonderful Love

Words: Robert Walmsley (1831-1905)
Music: F.L. Wiseman (1858-1944)

Capo 3 (C)

1. Come let us sing of a won-der-ful love, ten - der and true; out of the heart of the Fa - ther a - bove, stream - ing to me and to you: won - der - ful

2. Je - sus, the Sa - viour, this gos-pel to tell, joy - ful - ly came; came with the help-less and hope-less to dwell, shar - ing their sor - row and shame: seek - ing the

3. Je - sus is seek-ing the wn-der-ers yet; why do they roam? Love on - ly wait to for - give and for - get; home! wea - ry wan-der-ers, home! Won - der - ful

4. Come to my heart, O thou won-der-ful love, come and a - bide, lift - ing my life till it ris - es a - bove en - vy and false-hood and pride: seek - ing to

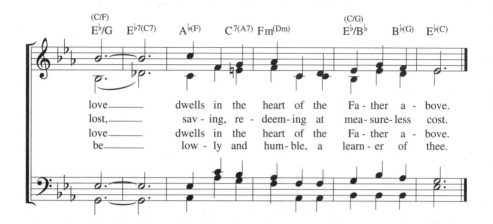

love_____	dwells in the	heart of the	Fa - ther a - bove.
lost,_____	sav - ing, re - deem- ing at	mea- sure- less	cost.
love_____	dwells in the	heart of the	Fa - ther a - bove.
be_____	low - ly and	hum- ble, a	learn - er of thee.

20a   Profession of faith Lord

You have always given Bread for the coming day,
and though I am poor,
today I believe.

Lord You have always given Peace for the coming day,
and though of anxious heart,
today I believe.

Lord, You have always kept me safe in trials,
and now, tried as I am,
today I believe.

Lord, You have always marked the road for the coming day,
and though it may be hidden,
today I believe.

Lord, You have always lightened this darkness of mine,
and though the night is here,
today I believe.

Lord, You have always spoken when time was ripe,
and though You be silent now,
today I believe.

Evening Prayer from the Northumbrian Office, Celtic Daily Prayer
© Northumbria Community Trust

21 Crown Him With Many Crowns

Words: Matthew Bridges & Godfrey Thring
in this version Jubilate Hymns
Music: George Elvey Arr. Roger Mayor

With Strength ♩ = 120

1. Crown him with ma - ny crowns, the Lamb up - on his
2. Crown him the Lord of life tri - umph - ant from the
3. Crown him the Lord of love, who shows his hands and
4. Crown him the Lord of peace - his king - dom is at
5. Crown him the Lord of years, the po - ten - tate of

throne, while heaven's e - ter - nal an - them drowns all mu - sic but its
grave, who rose vic - to - rious from the— strife for those he came to
side - those wounds yet vi - si - ble a - bove in beau - ty glo - ri -
hand; from pole to pole let war - fare— cease and Christ rule ev - ery
time, cre - a - tor of the rol - ling spheres in ma - jes - ty sub-

22 Face To Face

Chris Bowater

1. Face to face,— heart to heart,— let-ting your love— touch ev-ery part.— Draw-ing near,— you draw near to me;— you are al-ways— there, I don't al-ways— see. Face to face,— heart to heart,— this is

2. Face to face,— hand in hand,— hear-ing you say— "I un-der-stand."— Here with you,— my love, my friend;— sa-vour-ing— the— time, not want-ing it to— end. Face to face,— hand in hand,— this is

This song is recorded on the Spring Harvest 1998 New Songs Album.

23 Faithful One

With feeling ♩ = 96

Brian Doerksen

Faith - ful One, so un-chang - ing;_____ age - less One, you're my rock_____ of_____ peace._____ Lord of all, I de - pend on you, I call out to

when I fall down; all through the storm your love is the anchor my hope is in you alone.

Bridges — From C

24 Far And Near
(Say It Loud)

From Palms 96 & 98
Graham Kendrick

♩ = 72

Verse

1. Far and near hear the call, wor-ship him, Lord of all; fa-mi-lies of na-tions come ce-le-brate what God has done.
2. Deep and wide is the love hea-ven sent from a-bove; God's own Son for sin-ners died, rose a-gain – he is a-live.
3. At his name, let praise be-gin o-ceans roar, na-ture sings; for he comes to judge the earth in right-eous-ness and in his truth.

Repeat 1st time only

Say it loud, say it strong, tell the

This song is recorded on the Spring Harvest 1997 Live Worship Album - Volume 1.

25 Father God

This song is recorded on the Spring Harvest 1996 Live Worship Album - Volume 2.

25a   Working Together for God

Will you work together as the body of Christ in your various places,
putting aside personal preferences and desires,
for the sake of those for whom our Lord Jesus was willing to die?
We will work together, seeking the lost and serving all people.

Will you pray earnestly for gifts of the Holy Spirit which will
equip you for this task, and make you fruitful in the work of God?
We will seek his gifts and serve God's purpose.

Will you undertake this with your eyes fixed on Jesus,
ready to follow him through suffering and joy,
offering yourselves as a living sacrifice?
**We will go forward with him, confident
in his risen presence to sustain us.**

© Mark Earey

26 Father, Hear Our Prayer

Andy Piercy
Arr. Alison Berry

Meditatively ♩=100

Fa-ther, hear— our prayer— that our lives— may be— con-se-cra-ted on-ly un-to you.— Cleanse us with— your fire,— fill us with— your power— that the world— may glo-ri-fy— your name.—

This song is recorded on the Spring Harvest 1996 New Songs Album.

Lord, have mer - cy on us.

Christ, have mer - cy on us.

Lord, have mer - cy on us.

26a   The Gospel of God
from Romans 1

Let's affirm our trust in God

We have put our faith
in the gospel of God,
promised beforehand through his prophets
in the holy scriptures.
It is the gospel of his Son
Jesus Christ our Lord
according to the flesh
he was descended from David;
according to the Spirit
he was declared to be the powerful Son of God
by resurrection from the dead.

27 Father, I Can't Explain
(Faithful Father)

of praise to you, for who you are and all that you do.

From the mo-ment my life be-gan you have been faith-

To repeat

D.C.

Last time

- ful. ful.

You will be faith - ful, for-ev-er faith-

- ful. My Fa - ther.

28 For Ev'ry Worry
(The Name That Is Higher)

Rachel Lynes

bow to— the great-er— au-tho-ri-ty; emp-ty— re-li-gion— be-
lay at— the feet of— the ri-sen Lord; en-vy— and bit-ter-ness,

ware and— take— heed: the name of— Lord Je-sus— is high-er.
let this— be— known: the name of— Lord Je-sus— is high-er.

Chorus

His is— the name that— can streng-then— and heal, his is— the name to

which we kneel. Je-ho-vah— Sha-lom, you're— the God of— our— peace and

we lift— your name ev-en high-er.

29 Freedom From Captivity
(Wild Hope)

Jenny Baker
Arr. R Spencer

1. Free - dom from cap - ti - vi - ty,___ light___ in your dark -
2. Pride in - stead of burn - ing shame,_ com - fort in your griev -
(3) lon - ger will your name be pain,_ no more be de - feat -

- ness;___ I'll lift you out of ash - es___ and
- ing;_ I'll a - noint with oil of glad - ness___ to
- ed; I've chos - en to re-store___ you___ and

1. make you beau - ti - ful.___
take a - way your tears._
call you child of mine._

2.,3. Chorus
And I'll give you hope,_

wild hope, hope in the face of de -

- spair, a gar- ment of praise for a spi- rit of

hea - vi- ness.————————— 3. No

29a One thing I seek
from Psalm 27 and Mark 1

One thing I have asked of the Lord,
this is what I seek
that I may dwell in the house of the Lord
all the days of my life;
to behold the beauty of the Lord
and to seek him in his temple.

Who is it that you seek? **We seek the Lord our God.**

Do you seek him with all your heart? **We do. Lord have mercy.**

Do you seek him with all your soul? **We do. Lord have mercy.**

Do you seek him with all your mind? **We do. Lord have mercy.**

Do you seek him with all your strength? **We do. Lord have mercy.**

**The Lord is our light and our salvation; whom shall we fear?
The Lord is the stronghold of our lives; we shall not be
afraid. Amen.**

© Celtic Daily Prayer - A Northumbrian Office, Andy Raine and John T Skinner, compilers (Marshall Pickering, 1994). © Nether Springs Trust 1994., adapted and additional material Mark Earey

30 Give Me A Heart Of Compassion
(Enable Your Servants)

Driving, building with each verse

Jim Bailey

1. Give me a heart of com - pas - sion,
2. I'll sing the songs of sal - va - tion,
3. We're mov - ing for - ward to - geth - er,

give me a hope for the lost, give me a pas - sion for
bold - ly I'll speak out your word; I'll let them know by my
as one voice bold - ly pro - claim; the old and the young will be

those who are bro - ken and down.
life, I will show you are Lord.
strong and we'll lift up your name.

Lord, I am rea - dy and wil- ling to serve the weak and the
I'll tell them all a - bout Je - sus, I'll tell them all a - bout
On to the streets to the peo- ple, ev - ery man, wo- man and

This song is recorded on the Spring Harvest 1998 New Songs Album.

71

31 Go Forth And Tell

Words: James Seddon
Music: Michael Baughen
Arr. Christopher Norton

1. Go forth and tell! O church of God, a-wake!
2. Go forth and tell! God's love em-bra-ces all:
3. Go forth and tell! Where still the dark-ness lies,
4. Go forth and tell! The doors are o-pen wide:
5. Go forth and tell! O church of God, a-rise!

God's sav-ing news to all the na-tions
he will in grace re-spond to all who
in wealth or want, the sin-ner sure-ly
share God's good gifts - let no-one be de-
Go in the strength which Christ your Lord sup-

take: pro - claim Christ   Je - sus,   Sav - iour,
call: how   shall they   call   if   they have
dies: give us,   O   Lord, con - cern of
nied: live out   your   life   as   Christ your
plies: go   'til all   na - tions his great

Lord   and   King,   that   all   the   world___ his
ne - ver   heard   the   gra - cious in - vi -
heart   and   mind,   a   love like yours___ com -
Lord   shall choose,   your   ran - somed powers___ for
name   a - dore   and   serve him, Lord___ and

wor - thy praise___ may   sing.
ta - tion of___   his   word?
pas - sion - ate___ and   kind.
his   sole glo - ry   use.
King for   ev - er -   more.

32 God, We Praise You

Words: Christopher Idle
Music: Ludwig Van Beethoven
Arr. Christopher Norton

1. God, we praise you! God, we bless you! God, we name you
2. True a-pos-tles, faith-ful pro-phets, saints who set their
3. Je-sus Christ, the King of Glo-ry ev-er-last-ing
4. Christ, at God's right hand vic-tor-ious, you will judge the

Sove-reign Lord! Migh-ty King whom an-gels wor-ship,
world a-blaze, mar-tyrs, once un - known, un-heed-ed,
Son of God, hum-ble was your vir-gin mo-ther,
world you made: Lord, in mer-cy help your ser-vants

75

33 God Is Good All The Time

Don Moen &
Paul Overstreet

78

34 Great Is The Darkness
(Come, Lord Jesus)

With strength ♩ = 140

Noel Richards & Gerald Coates
Arr. Leon Evans

1. Great is— the dark - ness— that cov - ers— the earth, op - pres - sion,— in - jus - tice— and pain; na - tions— are slip - ping— in hope - less— de - spair, though ma - ny— have

2. May now— your church rise— with pow - er— and love, this glo - ri - ous gos - pel— pro - claim; in ev - ery na - tion— sal - va - tion— will come to those who— be -

3. Great ce - le - bra - tions— on that fi - nal day, when out of— the hea - vens— you come; dark - ness— will van - ish,— all sor - row— will end, and ru - lers— will

come in   your   name -
- lieve in   your   name.
bow at   your   throne;

watch - ing   while   san - i - ty   dies,
Help   us   bring   light   to   this   world,
our   great   com - mis - sion   com - plete;

touched   by   the   mad - ness   and   lies.
that   we   might   speed   your   re - turn.
then   face   to   face   we   shall   meet.

Come,   Lord   Je - sus,   come,   Lord   Je - sus,

pour out— your Spi - rit— we pray;

come, Lord Je - sus, come, Lord Je - sus,

pour out— your Spi - rit on us to - day.—

34a A call to obedience

My soul's desire is to see the face of God
     and to rest in His house.
My soul's desire is to study the Scriptures
     and to learn the ways of God.
My soul's desire is to be freed from all fear and sadness,
     and to share Christ's risen life.
My soul's desire is to imitate my King,
     and to sing His purposes always.
My soul's desire is to enter the gates of heaven
     and to gaze upon the light that shines forever.
I trust in Thee, O Lord. I say, Thou art my God.
My times are in Thy hand, my times are in Thy hand.

A call to obedience, the Hild liturgy from the Northumbrian Office, Celtic Night Prayer
© Northumbria Community Trust

35 Great Is The Lord

Great—— is the Lord— and most wor-thy of praise, the
ci-ty of our God, the ho-ly place, the joy of the— whole earth.—
Great———— is the
Lord in whom we have— the vic - to - ry!—— He
aids us a-gainst— the e - ne - my, we bow down on— our knees.—

36 Great Is Your Faithfulness

Words: Thomas Chisholm (1866-1960)
Music: William Runyan (1870-1957)
Arr. Roger Mayor

Prayerfully ♩ = 100

1. Great is your faith - ful - ness, O God my Fa - ther,
2. Sum - mer and win - ter, and spring-time and har - vest,
3. Par - don for sin, and a peace ev - er - last - ing,

you have ful - filled all your pro - mise to me;
sun, moon and stars in their cour - ses a - bove
your liv - ing pre - sence to cheer and to guide;

you ne - ver fail and your love is un - chang - ing -
join with all na - ture in e - lo - quent wit - ness
strength for to - day and bright hope for to - mor - row -

all you have been, you for ev - er will be.
to your great faith - ful - ness, mer - cy and love.
these are the bless - ings your love will pro - vide.

36a Spiritual warfare
from Colossians 2: 15

And having disarmed the powers and authorities, he made a public spectacle of them, triumphing over them by the cross.

37 Guide Me, O My Great Redeemer

Words: Peter Williams and others
Music: John Hughes
Arr. Christopher Norton

Steadily ♩ = 102

1. Guide me, O my great Redeemer, pilgrim through this barren land:
   I am weak, but you are mighty - hold me with your
2. Open now the crystal fountain where the healing waters flow;
   let the fiery, cloudy pillar lead me all my
3. When I tread the verge of Jordan bid my anxious fears subside;
   Death of death, and hell's Destruction, land me safe on

38 Have You Heard The Good News?

Stuart Garrard

♩ = 140

Have you— heard the good— news,— have you— heard the good— news?— We can— live— in— hope— be-cause of— what the— Lord— has— done.— Have you—

1. There is a— way— when there— seems—
2. A hope for— jus - tice

This song is recorded on the Spring Harvest 1996 Live Worship Album - Volume 2 and the 1996 Praise Mix.

89

39 He Bought Me To His Banqueting
Table *(His Banner Over Me)*

Song of Songs 2:4
Kevin Prosch

This song is recorded on the Spring Harvest 1995 Live Worship Album and the 1995 Praise Mix.

And we can feel the love— of God— in this place: we be-lieve your good-ness, we re-ceive your grace; we de-light our-selves— at your ta-ble, O God,— you do all things well— just look at our lives.—

MEN: He

40

He Has Risen

Noel & Tricia Richards
& Gerald Coates
Arr. Ian Hannah

This song is recorded on the Spring Harvest 1994 Live Worship Album and the 1994 New Songs Album.

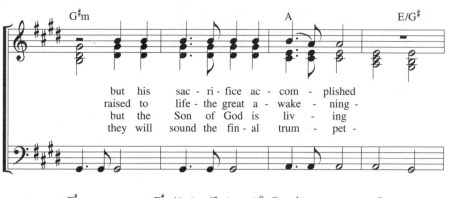

but his   sac - ri - fice ac - com - plished
raised to   life - the great a - wake - ning -
but the   Son of God is   liv - ing
they will   sound the fin - al   trum - pet -

vict - ory ov - er sin and hell._____
Sa - tan's power he ov - er - came._____
so our hope is not in vain._____
from the grave we shall a - rise._____

5. He has given life immortal,
   we shall see him face to face;
   through eternity we'll praise him,
   Christ the champion of our faith.

40a   To Know Christ More

Lord Jesus Christ,
we thank you for all the benefits you have won for us,
for all the pains and insults you have borne for us.
Most merciful redeemer,
friend and brother,
may we know you more clearly,
love you more dearly,
and follow you more nearly,
day by day. Amen.

St Richard of Chichester, 1197-1253

41
He Is The Lord
(Show Your Power)

Kevin Prosch

This song is recorded on the Spring Harvest 1995 Praise Mix.

4th time - to Coda

1.3.

97

42 He Rescued Me

Country rock style

Geoff Baker

He res-cued me from the dark - est night and brought me in to his glo - rious light; to know his pre - sence is my de - light, al - le - lu - ia, he res-cued me.

1. A joy that keeps o - ver - flow-ing,
2. The Fa - ther's arms are a - round me,
3. To Je - sus Christ be the glo - ry,

This song is recorded on the Spring Harvest 1998 r:age Album.

a peace words can-not ex-press,   my sin and guilt are
the Spi-rit's ful-ness with-in: no con-dem-na-tion
al-migh-ty Sa-viour and friend;   the love that bought me

washed a-way,   I share his righ-teous-ness.
now I fear,   I rest se-cure in him.
with his blood   will keep me to the end.

He res-cued lu-ia, he res-cued me,___ al-le-

lu-ia, he res-cued me,___ al-le-lu-ia, he res-cued me.___

43 He's Given His All
(A Worshipping Heart)

Jill Sutheran

He's giv-en his all,— done it for me,— whipped and scorned— he died on a tree.— Giv-ing his love,— his pow-er and grace,— that we might live,— he died in our place.— A wor-ship-ping— heart— is what he— de-serves, a wor-ship-ping— heart— my place he's— re-

served, a wor-ship-ping heart, in spi-rit and truth, a wor-ship-ping heart, a wor-ship-ping heart is what he de-serves.

1. He's giv-en his all,

44 He's Given Me A Garment Of Praise
(Garment Of Praise)

From Isiah 61:3&10
David Hadden

This song is recorded on the Spring Harvest 1997 New Songs Album.

he's giv-en me a -pair. He's giv-en me a

gar-ment of praise in - stead of a spi - rit of des-

- pair; he's giv-en me a

gar-ment of praise in - stead of a spi - rit of des-

pair.

106

45 Hear Our Cry

Graham Kendrick

WOMEN:
Hear our cry, O hear our cry: 'Je-sus, come!' Hear our cry, O

MEN:
hear our cry: 'Je - sus, come!'

MEN:
1. The tide of prayer is ris - ing, a deep - er—
come! 2. We lift our eyes with long - ing to see your—
come! 3. The streets of teem - ing ci - ties cry out for—
come! 4. Re - fresh them with your pre - sence, give grace for—

pas - sion burn - ing -
king - dom com - ing -
heal - ing ri - vers -
deep re - pen - tance -

WOMEN:
Hear our cry, O hear our cry: 'Je - sus,

MEN:

MEN: ALL:
come! 5. Tear back the shroud of sha - dows that cov - ers
come! 6. Re - veal - ing your sal - va - tion in ev - ery

all the peo - ples - Hear our cry, O hear our cry: 'Je - sus,
tribe and na - tion - Hear our cry, O hear our cry: 'Je - sus,

WOMEN: MEN:
come!' Hear our cry, O hear our cry: 'Je - sus, hear our cry: 'Je - sus, come!'

45a Prayer for discernment

O God our disturber,
whose speech is pregnant with power
and whose word will be fulfilled;
may we know ourselves unsatisfied
with all that distorts your truth,
and make our hearts attentive
to your liberating voice,
in Jesus Christ. Amen.

© All Desires Known, Janet Morley (Movement for the Ordination of Women, 1988). © Janet Morley 1988

46 Heavenly Father, How I Worship

Geoff Baker

111

47   Heavenly Father

113

I will thirst for you from the depths of my soul, I will worship you 'til the end of time.

114

48 Here I Am Once Again
(Pour Out My Heart)

Craig Musseau

Here I am once a-gain,—— I pour out my heart— for I know that you hear— ev-ery cry, you are lis-ten-ing no mat-ter what state—— my heart is in.— You are faith - ful to an-swer with

This song is recorded on the Spring Harvest 1998 New Songs Album and the 1998 r:age Album.

48a Great and Wonderful

from Revelation 15

Great and wonderful are your deeds, Lord God the Almighty
just and true are your ways, O King of the nations.
You have given us new life and hope
by raising Jesus from the dead.
Alleluia! Christ is risen.
He is risen indeed. Alleluia!

Mark Earey, using Alternative Service Book 1980. © Central Board of Finance of the Church of England 1980. and traditional material

49 Hold Me Closer
(May I Never Lose Sight)

Noel & Tricia Richards

Hold me clos-er to you each day; may my love for you ne-ver fade; keep my fo-cus on all that's true; may I ne-ver lose sight of you.

1. In my fail-ure, in my success,
2. You are on-ly a breath a-way,
3. No one loves me the way you do,

if in sad-ness or hap - pi - ness,—
watch-ing ov-er me ev - ery day;—
no one cares for me like you do;—

be the hope I am cling - ing to,— for my
in my heart I am filled with peace when I
feels like heav-en has brok - en through;— God, you

heart be - longs to you.—
hear you speak to me.—
know how I love you.—

49a   Sharing the Peace of Christ
from Colossians 3.14

To crown all things there must be love,
to bind all together and complete the whole.
Let the peace of Christ rule in your hearts.
The peace of the Lord be always with you.
And also with you.

© Patterns for Worship (Church House Publishing, 1995). © Central Board of Finance of the
Church of England 1989, 1995.

50 Holy, Holy, Holy, Lord God Almighty

Words: Reginald Heber
in this version Jubilate Hymns
Music: John Bacchus Dykes

♩ = 95

1. Ho-ly, ho-ly, ho-ly, Lord___ God al-migh-ty! Ear-ly in the morn-ing our song of praise shall be: ho-ly, ho-ly,
2. Ho-ly, ho-ly, ho-ly! All the saints a-dore you, cast-ing down their ro-yal crowns a-round the glas-sy sea, cher-u-bim and
3. Ho-ly, ho-ly, ho-ly! Though the dark-ness hide you, though the sin-ful hu-man eye your glo-ry may not see, you a-lone are
4. Ho-ly, ho-ly, ho-ly, Lord___ God al-migh-ty! All your works shall praise your name, in earth and sky and sea: ho-ly, ho-ly,

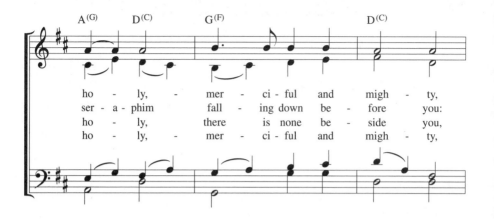

ho - ly, - mer - ci - ful and migh - ty,
ser - a - phim fall - ing down be - fore you:
ho - ly, there is none be - side you,
ho - ly, - mer - ci - ful and migh - ty,

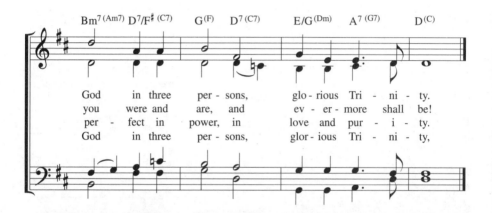

God in three per - sons, glo - rious Tri - ni - ty.
you were and are, and ev - er - more shall be!
per - fect in power, in love and pur - i - ty.
God in three per - sons, glor - ious Tri - ni - ty,

50a　All that I am

All that I am, Lord. I place into Your hands;
all that I do, Lord, I place into Your hands.
Everything I work for I place into Your hands;
everything I hope for I place into Your hands.
The troubles that weary me I place into Your hands;
the thoughts that disturb me I place into Your hands.
Each that I pray for I place into Your hands;
each that I care for I place into Your hands.

A call to Humility, the Oswald liturgy from the Northumbrian Office, Celtic Night Prayer ©
Northumbria Community Trust

51 How Deep The Father's Love

Thoughtfully ♩ = 112

Stuart Townend

1. How deep the Fa-ther's love for us, how vast be-yond all mea-sure, that he should give his on-ly Son to make a wretch his trea - sure. How great the pain of sear-ing loss: the Fa-ther turns his face a-
2. Be - hold the man up - on a cross, my sin up - on his should - ers; a - shamed, I hear my mock-ing voice call out a - mong the scoff - ers. It was my sin that held him there un - til it was ac-com -
3. I will not boast in an - y - thing, no gifts, no power, no wis - dom; but I will boast in Je - sus Christ, his death and re - sur - rec - tion. Why should I gain from his re - ward? I can-not give an ans -

This song is recorded on the Spring Harvest 1997 Live Worship Album - Volume 1.

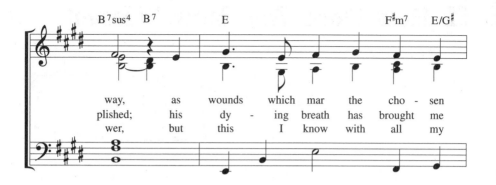

way,   as   wounds   which   mar   the   cho - sen
plished;   his   dy - ing   breath   has   brought   me
wer,   but   this   I   know   with   all   my

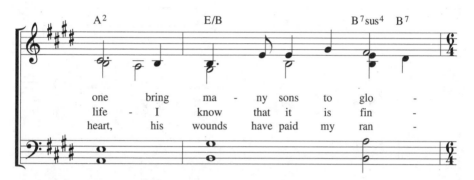

one   bring   ma - ny   sons   to   glo -
life - I   know   that   it   is   fin -
heart,   his   wounds   have paid   my   ran -

- ry.
- ished.
- som.

![51a Salvation banner]
51a   Salvation
from Colossians 1: 19-20

For God was pleased to have all his fulness dwell in him, and through him to reconcile to himself all things, whether things on earth or things in heaven, by making peace through his blood, shed on a cross.

52 How Good And How Pleasant

From Psalm 133
Graham Kendrick

♩ = 126

1. How good and how plea-sant— it is—
2. How deep are the ri - vers— that run—

when we— all live—— in u - ni - ty—— re -
when we— are one—— in Je - sus—— and

fresh - ing as dew at— the dawn,— like
share with the Fa - ther— and Son— the

rare a - noint - ing oil—— up - on— the head.—
bles - sings of— his ev - er - last - ing life.—

This song is recorded on the Spring Harvest 1996 Live Worship Album - Volume 1.

53   How Wonderful

As a jig ♩ = 126

Dave Bilbrough

How— won - der - ful,— how— glo - ri - ous— is— the love of— God,— bring - ing— heal - ing,— for - give - ness— won - der - ful love.

Let ce - le - bra - tion— e - cho
We pro - claim— the king - dom— of our
List - en to the mu - sic— as his

This song is recorded on the Spring Harvest 1995 Live Worship Album.

through————— this— land:— we bring re - con - ci - li - a -
God————— is— here;— come and join— the heaven - ly an -
prais - es fill the— air;— with joy————— and with glad-

- tion,— we bring hope——— to ev - ery one.——— How—
- them— ring - ing loud——— and ring - ing clear.———
- ness— tell the peo - ple ev - ery - where:———

53a   The Apostles' Creed

I believe in God, the Father almighty,
creator of heaven and earth.
I believe in Jesus Christ, his only Son, our Lord.
He was conceived by the power of the Holy Spirit
and born of the Virgin Mary.
He suffered under Pontius Pilate,
was crucified, died and was buried.
On the third day he rose again.
He ascended into heaven,
and is seated at the right hand of the Father.
He will come again to judge the living and the dead.
I believe in the Holy Spirit, the holy catholic Church,
the communion of the saints, the forgiveness of sins,
the resurrection of the body, and the life everlasting.
Amen.

© 1970, 1971, 1975 International Consultation on English Texts (ICET)

54 How Lovely Is Your Dwelling Place
(Better Is One Day)

Slowly, with awe

Matt Redman

1. How love-ly is your dwel-ling place, O Lord— Al-migh-ty;— my soul longs and ev-en faints for you, for here my heart is sat-is-fied with-in— your pre-sence.— I sing be-neath the sha-dow of your wings. Bet-ter is

Bridge

My heart and flesh cry out for you, the liv-ing God;

your Spi-rit's wa-ter for my soul.

I've tas-ted and I've seen, come once a-gain to me;

I will draw near to you, I will draw near to you.

Bet-ter is else-where.

130

55 I Believe In God The Father
(Apostle's Creed)

Wayne Drain

I be-lieve in God— the Fa - ther, I be-lieve in Je- sus_ the Son,_

- lieve! *(Tacet.)*

I be - lieve in God the Ho - ly Spi - rit,

I be- lieve_ in the Three in One.

1. Verse I be - lieve he was born— of— a vir - gin, was

cru - ci - fied— and bu - ried in— the ground,— de-

scend-ed in - to hell— and won the bat - tle, but the

de-vil, death— and hell— could-n't hold— him down.

O Lord, we're drown-ing in— con-fu - sion, so

ma - ny of— us go-ing se - parate ways;—

want - ing to— be god— is our— de-lu - sion, but

56 I Dream Of Tongues Of Fire
(Believer)

With energy

Matt Redman

1. I dream of tongues of fi - re   rest-ing on your peo-ple,
2. I hope to see you come down,   rend the migh - ty heav-ens,
3. May your church now reach out,   sow-ing truth and jus-tice,

I dream of all the mi - ra - cles ___ to come.
and let your gl - ory cov - er all ___ the earth;
learn to love the poor and help ___ the weak.

I hope to see the com - ing   heal - ing of the na - tions,
to see your sons and daught-ers   come to know and love you,
When your king-dom's com - ing   it will touch the brok - en,

I long to see the pro - di - gals ___ re - turn.
and find a pur - er pas - sion in ___ the church.
place the lone - ly in a fa - mi - ly.

This song is recorded on the Spring Harvest 1998 New Songs Album.

So ma - ny hopes___ and long - ings in you;___
These are the things___ my heart___ will pur - sue:___
So ma - ny hopes___ and long - ings in you:___

— when will all the dreams come true? I'm a be - liev-

- er in your king - dom, I am a seek - er of the new things,

I am a dream - er with some old dreams, let them now come.___
(Will you now come?)___

57 I Give You All The Honour

1 Chron 16:25-27
Luke 4:18-21
Carl Tuttle

1. I give you all the hon-our____ and praise that's due your
Spi-rit moves up-on me now,_ you meet my deep-est
bro-ken chains that bound me,____ you've set this cap-tive

name: for you are the King of glo-ry,____ the cre-
need; and I lift my hands up to your throne-____ your
free; I will lift my voice to praise your name__ for

a-tor of all things._____ And I
mer-cy I've re-ceived._____
all e-ter-ni-ty._____

wor-ship you,_____ I give my life to you_____

58 I Know That My Redeemer Lives

Words: Samuel Medley (1738-99)
Music: W Youens, 1889

1. I know that my____ Re - deem - er
2. He lives, to bless____ me with his
3. He lives, and grants____ me dai - ly
4. He lives, all glo - ry to his

lives - what joy____ the blessed____ as - sur - rance gives!
love; he lives,____ to plead____ for me____ a - bove;
breath; he lives,____ and I____ shall con - quer death;
name; he lives,____ my Sa - viour, still____ the same.

He lives, he lives,____ who once was dead; he
he lives, my hun - gry soul to feed; he
he lives, my man - sion to pre - pare; he
What joy the blessed____ as - sur - rance gives, I

138

58a   World Mission
from Colossians 1: 27-29

To them God has chosen to make known among the Gentiles the glorious riches of this mystery, which is Christ in you, the hope of glory. We proclaim him, admonishing and teaching everyone with all wisdom, so that we may present everyone perfect in Christ. To this end I labour, struggling with all his energy, which so powerfully works in me.

59   I Need You

Chris Bowater

I need you like dew in the de - sert, like re-
fresh - ing sum - mer rain,— come and pour your love a- gain— on
me.— I'm find - ing that ev - 'ry time— I come and
ask for some - thing more you ne - ver fail— to pour your

Bridges — From D

60 I Need You More

Gently ♩ = 112

Lindell Cooley
& Bruce Haynes

nev - er want— to go— back— to my old life—

I need— you Lord. Right here in your

pre-sence is where I— be-long;———— this old bro-ken

heart has fi - nal-ly found— a home,———————— and I'll

nev - er be— a-lone.———————— I need— you Lord.—

61   I See The Lord

From Isaiah 6
Chris Falson

This song is recorded on the Spring Harvest 1996 Live Worship Album - Volume 1 and the 1996 Praise Mix.

62 I Want To Be Out Of My Depth In Your Love

Noel Richards
& Doug Horley

Gently ♩ = 100

Learn-ing to let— you lead,— put-ting all trust—
Things I have held— so tight,— made my se-cu-

— in you;— deep-er in-to— your arms,—
— ri-ty;— give me the strength— I need—

sur-round-ed by you.
to sim-ply let go.—

62a   Keep your people, Lord

Keep your people, Lord, in the arms of your embrace;
shelter them under your wings.
Be their light in darkness,
be their hope in distress,
be their calm in anxiety.
Be strength in their weakness,
be their comfort in pain,
be their song in the night.

From the Ita Compline from the Northumbrian Office, Celtic Night Prayer © Northumbria
Community Trust

63 I Will Dance
(Undignified)

2 Samuel 6:22
Matt Redman

♩ = 112

I will dance, I will sing, to be mad for my King; no-thing, Lord is hin-der-ing the pas-sion in my soul.— pas-sion in my soul.— And I'll be-come___ ev-en more un-dig-ni-fied than this; some would say it's fool-ish-ness, but I'll be-come___

151

64 I Will Follow You
(Lay Myself Down)

Sue Rinaldi
& Caroline Bonnett

With feeling ♩ = 70

I will fol-low you to the cross— and lay my-self down,—

lay my-self down.— I will fol-low you to the cross— and

lay my-self down,— lay my-self down. 1. Rid me— of— these— dir-
2. Kiss me— with— your— heal-

- ty—clothes, cleanse me—from all— this pol-lu - tion.—— I choose—
- ing— touch,— take me— to the—heat of your— fire,—— bathe me—

This song is recorded on the Spring Harvest 1998 r:age Album and the 1998 Praise Mix.

65 I Will Sing The Wondrous Story

Words: F. W. Rawley
Music: R.H. Prichard

1. I will sing— the won-drous sto-ry of the
2. I was lost,— but Je-sus found— me, found the
3. I was faint— and fears pos-ses-sed me, I was
4. Days of dark-ness still may meet— me, sor-row's
5. He will keep— me 'til the ri-ver rolls its

Christ who died— for me; how he left— the
sheep that went— a-stray; raised me up— and
bruised from ma-ny a fall; hope was gone,— and
path I oft-en tread; but his pres-ence
wa-ters at— my feet; then at last— he'll

realms of glo-ry for the cross of Cal-va-ry:
gent-ly led— me back in-to the nar-row way.
shame dis-tressed— me, but his love has par-doned all:
still is with— me, by his guid-ing hand— I'm led;
bring me o-ver saved by grace and made— com-plete.

Yes, I'll sing the won-drous sto-ry of the Christ who died for me, sing it with the saints in glo - ry ga - thered by the cry-stal sea.

65a   Christ, Proclaimed

from 1 Timothy 3 & 2 Timothy 2

Let us declare our faith

We believe in one Lord, Jesus Christ
he was revealed in the flesh,
attested by the Spirit, seen by angels,
proclaimed among the nations,
believed in throughout the world, and taken up to glory.

If we died with him, **we shall live with him.**
If we endure, **we shall reign with him. Amen.**

66   I Will Offer Up My Life

Matt Redman

1. I will of-fer up my
2. You de-serve my ev-ery

life in spi-rit and truth,—— pour-ing out the oil of
breath for you've paid the great cost - giv-ing up your life to

love as my wor-ship to you.—— In sur-ren-der I must
death, ev-en death on a cross.—— You took all my shame a-

This song is recorded on the Spring Harvest 1996 Live Worship Album - Volume 1.

give my ev - ery part;___ Lord, re - ceive the sac - ri -
- way, there de - feat - ed my sin,___ o - pened up the gates of

- fice of a bro - ken heart.___ Je - sus, what can I give,___
heaven and have bec - koned me in.___

___ what can I bring___ to so faith - ful a friend,___

___ to so lov - ing a king?___ Sav - iour, what can be said,___

___ what can be sung___ as a praise of your name___

67   I Will Worship

David Ruis

This song is recorded on the Spring Harvest 1996 Praise Mix.

all my— wor - ship, I will give— you all my— praise;—

— you a- lone— I long to— wor - ship, you a- lone— are

wor - thy— of— my—— praise.——

68 I Worship You, Almighty God

Ex 15:11, Ps 71:19
Sandra Corbett

I wor-ship you, al-migh-ty God,___ there is none like you; I wor-ship you, O Prince of Peace-___ that is what I love to do. I give you praise,___ for you are my right-eous-ness;___ I wor-ship you, al-migh-ty God,___ there is none like you.

69 It's Our Confession, Lord
(Sweet Mercies)

David Ruis

It's our con-fess-ion, Lord,— that we— are weak,— so ve-ry weak,— but you are— strong;— and though we've no-thing, Lord,— to lay at your feet,— we come to your feet and say: 'Help us a-long.'—

sweet mer- cies flow from hea - ven, new mer- cies for to- day:— O

show- er them down,— Lord, as we pray.'—— Let your mer- cies fall from hea- ven,

sweet mer- cies flow from hea - ven, new mer- cies for to- day:— O

D.S. al Coda

show- er them down,— Lord, as we pray.'——

⊕ Coda

70 Is It True Today
(History Maker)

Martin Smith

Is it true — to-day that when peo-
— to-day that when peo-

- ple pray cloud-less skies — will break
- ple pray we'll see dead — men rise

kings and queens — will shake? Yes, it's true
and the blind — set free? Yes, it's true —

— and I be-lieve — it, —
— and I be-lieve — it, —

This song is recorded on the Spring Harvest 1998 Praise Mix.

71 It's Rising Up

Matt Redman
& Martin Smith

It's ris-ing up from coast to coast, from north to south, and east to west; the cry of hearts that love your name, which with one voice we will pro-claim. The for-mer things have ta-ken place: can

This song is recorded on the Spring Harvest 1996 New Songs Album and the 1996 Praise Mix.

u - shers— in— your— king - dom— rule?— O,

let the— cry— to nations— ring,— that all may— come— and

all may—sing:— 'Je - sus is— a -

live, Je - sus is— a -

live!'

173

72
Jesus Christ
(Once Again)

Matt Redman

1. Je - sus Christ, I think up - on your sa - cri - fice:
2. Now you are ex - alt - ed to the high - est place -

you be - came no - thing, poured out to death.
King of the heav - ens - where one day I'll bow,

Ma - ny times I've won - dered at your gift of life, and
but for now, I mar - vel at this sav - ing grace, and

I'm in that place once a - gain,
I'm full of praise once a - gain,

This song is recorded on the Spring Harvest 1997 New Songs Album and 1997 Live Worship Album - Volume 1.

175

73 Jesus Christ Rules Supreme

David Lyle Morris

Je - sus; through him to re - con - cile all things to God;—

a - tion, the Son of the Fa - ther cre - a - ted all things,

mak - ing our peace his blood shed on Cal - va - ry.

king-doms or powers, ru - lers or au - tho - ri - ties.

4. We have been giv - en all ful - ness in Christ,— with

2. Je - sus su - preme— be - fore all oth - er things; in

hearts and minds set on hea - ven. We may be ho - ly in

him all things hold to - ge - ther. He's the be- gin - ning, first -

our Fa - ther's sight,___ with - out a stain___

born from the dead,___ in ev - ery-thing,___

free from ac - cu - sa - tion.

he will have su- pre - ma - cy.

74 Jesus, Jesus, Holy And Anointed One

John Barnett

75 Jesus Is The Name We Honour
(We Will Glorify)

Brightly ♩ = 140 — Phil Lawson-Johnston

1. Je - sus is the name— we ho - nour,— Je - sus is the name— we praise.—
2. Je - sus is the name— we wor - ship;— Je - sus is the name— we trust.—
3. Je - sus is the Fa - ther's splen - dour,— Je - sus is the Fa - ther's joy.—

Ma - jes - tic name a - bove— all oth - er names;— the high - est heaven— and earth pro - claim— that
He is the King a - bove— all oth - er kings;— let all cre - a - tion stand and sing— that
He will re - turn to reign— in ma - je - sty,— and ev - ery eye— at last will see— that

76 Jesus, Lover Of My Soul

With feeling ♩ = 96

Paul Oakley

This song is recorded on the Spring Harvest 1997 New Songs Album.

- ga, you have loved— me,— and I will share— e- ter - ni- ty with—

— you.— It's all a- bout you,————— Je - sus,—

— and all this is for— you,————— for your glo - ry and— your fame;—

— it's not a- bout me,————— as if you— should do— things my— way -

you a- lone— are God— and I sur-ren - der———— to your— ways.—

77 Jesus Shall Take The Highest Honour

Chris Bowater

Je-sus shall take the high-est ho-nour,— Je-sus shall take the high-est praise. Let all earth join heaven in ex-alt-ing the name which is— a-bove all o-ther names.— Let's bow the knee— in hum-ble a-dor-a-tion,— for at his name— ev-ery knee— must bow;— let ev-ery tongue— con-fess he is

185

78   Jesus, The Name
Above All Other Names

David Hadden

Moderately

1. Je - sus, — the name a - bove all oth - er names, — migh - ty God, — Prince of Peace, my sa - viour. Je - sus, — I love you more and more — each day, — you're my King, — and Lord, I want to know you

2. Je - sus, — the ve - ry men - tion of — your name, — stirs my heart, — and Lord, I want to know you. Je - sus, — with all my heart I will — pro - claim — that you're my King, — and Lord, I want to know you

187

79 Jesus' Love Has Got Under Our Skin *(Under Our Skin)*

Graham Kendrick

Je - sus' love has got un - der our skin;

Je - sus' love has got un - der our skin -

Je - sus' deep-er than co-lour, oh,____ rich-er than

cul-ture, oh,____ strong-er than e - mo-tion, oh,____

____ wi- der than the o-cean, oh!____ Don't you want to

This song is recorded on the Spring Harvest 1997 Live Worship Album - Volume 2.

80 Jesus Your Beauty Is Filling This Temple *(Holy River)*

Sue Rinaldi
& Caroline Bonnett

1. Je - sus,— your beau - ty— is fill - ing— this tem - ple,— Je - sus,— your fra - grance— is draw - ing— me clos - er,— and with ev - ery step— I take— you lead me in- to this ho - ly— place—— and it wash- es me clean,—

2. Je - sus,— your pas - sion— is fill - ing— this tem - ple,— Je - sus,— your mer - cy— is draw - ing— me clos - er,— and with ev - ery step— I take— you lead me in- to a world— that— aches,—— and I can- not rest—

This song is recorded on the Spring Harvest 1998 r:age Album.

for my eyes have seen Mes - si - ah.
'til all eyes have seen Mes - si - ah.

And I will jump in - to the ho - ly ri - ver, I will

lose my-self to my de - live-rer; I will jump in - to the

ho - ly ri - ver, I will lose my-self to my de - live - rer.

In this ho - ly_ place I can see_ your_ face,_ Me-

192

81 Just Let Me Say

Geoff Bullock

82   Kings And Nations

Robin Mark

Steadily

Kings and na-tions all shall come, come and bow be-fore your throne; eve-ry tribe and eve-ry tongue wor-ship-ping our God a-lone. From

Zi-on, O Lord___ shall your name be told,___ to
sing of your love,___ through all of the earth,___ O
pre-cious Lamb,___ by your sa-cri-fice___ sal-
va-tion__ comes.__

197

83   Lamb Of God

Chris Bowater

Lamb of God,— ho - ly One,— Je - sus Christ— Son of God,— lift - ed up— will - ing- ly— to die——————————— that I the guil - ty one may know———— the blood once shed———— still free- ly flow- ing,— still

84

Let It Rain
(Love Rain Down)

Rhythmically

Joel Pott

Let it rain, let it rain,— let it rain, let it rain on ev-ery

na - tion.———— Let it rain, let it rain,— let it

1. rain, let it rain on ev-ery na - tion.———— Let it

2. na - tion.———— Verse

1. Take our hearts— as fuel—
2. Let there be— new hope—

84a   Christ, the image of God

from Colossians 1

We believe in Jesus Christ,
image of the invisible God, first-born of all creation,
in whom all things were made in heaven and earth;
seen and unseen;
states and powers, rulers and authorities;
all things were created through him and for him.
He is before all things, in him all things hold together.
He is the head of the church,
the beginning, and the first-born from the dead.

We believe in Jesus Christ,
image of the invisible God. Amen.

© Mark Earey, adapted from Bible Praying, Michael Perry (Fount, 1992). © Michael Perry

85 Living On The Edge Of Destiny
(Today, Let This Be The Day)

Chris Bowater

Steadily

1. Liv - ing on the edge of des - ti - ny,_ look-ing in the face of pro-mis-es;_
Break-ing through the haze of a - pa-thy,_ dawns a new day of ex-pec-tan-cy;_

we've nev-er been this way be-fore,_ it could ev-en be to-day._

2. More than the pow - er_ of po - si-tive thought,

more than a rea - son to be - lieve;_ a

86 Lord, For The Years

Words: Timothy Dudley-Smith
Music: Michael Baughen
Arr. Christopher Norton

Medium slow ♩ = 108

1. Lord, for the years your love has kept and guid - ed,
2. Lord, for that word, the word of life which fires_ us,
3. Lord, for our land, in this our ge - ne - ra - tion,
4. Lord, for our world, when we dis - own and doubt_ him,
5. Lord, for our - selves; in liv - ing power re - make_ us -

urged and in - spired us, cheered us on__ our way,
speaks to our hearts and sets our souls_ a - blaze,
spi - rits op - pressed by plea - sure, wealth_ and care;
love - less in strength, and com - fort - less_ in pain;
self on the cross and Christ up - on__ the throne,

C C/E F A⁷/E D D⁷/F♯ Gsus G

sought	us	and	saved	us,	par -	doned	and	pro -	vid -	ed,
teach -	es	and	trains,	re -	bukes	us	and	in -	spires	us;
for	young	and	old,	for	com -	mon - wealth	and	na -	tion,
hun -	gry	and	help -	less,	lost	in -	deed	with -	out	him,
past	put	be -	hind	us,	for	the	fu -	ture	take	us,

Am C/E F C/E Dm⁷ G⁷ C

Lord	of	the	years,	we	bring	our	thanks	to - day.
Lord	of	the	word,	re -	ceive	your	peo -	ple's praise.
Lord	of	our	land,	be	pleased	to	hear	our prayer.
Lord	of	the	world,	we	pray	that	Christ	may reign.
Lord	of	our	lives,	to	live	for	Christ	a - lone.

F   C   F G C

87 Lord, I Come To You
(The Power Of Your Love)

Geoff Bullock

1. Lord, I come to you,— let my heart be changed, re-newed,— flow-ing from the grace that I found— in you. And, Lord, I've come to know— the weak-ness-es I see in me— will be stripped a-way— in liv-ing ev-ery day—

2. Lord, un-veil my eyes,— let me see you face to face,— the know-ledge of your love, as you live— in me. Lord, re-new my mind— as your will un-folds in my life,— in liv-ing ev-ery day—

This song is recorded on the Spring Harvest 1997 Live Worship Album - Volume 1.

by the power of your love.

in the power of your love.

Hold me close,— let your love sur - round me,

bring me near,— draw me to your side; and

as I wait, — I'll rise up like the ea - gle, and I will soar with you;

your Spi-rit leads me on in the power of your love.

88 Lord, I Lift Your Name

from the earth___ to the cross,___ my debt___ to pay,___

from the cross___ to the grave,___ from the grave___ to the sky,___

Lord, I lift your name___ on___ high.___

88a   Family life

Almighty God,
who gave marriage to be a source of blessing,
we thank you for all the joys and sorrows of family life,
and ask for your help in times of trouble.
May we know your presence and peace in our homes;
fill them with your love,
and use them for your glory;
through Jesus Christ our Lord. Amen.

89 Lord, My Heart Before You
(Honest Heart)

Gently

Trish Morgan

Lord, my heart be-fore you is o-pen and bare.

I stand in need of your mer - cy, in need of your care. Wash my sins a - way in this fall - ing rain. In this day of

89a   Invocation of the Holy Spirit

Most powerful Holy Spirit, come down upon us
and subdue us.

From Heaven, where the ordinary
is made glorious, and glory seems
but ordinary,
bathe us with the brilliance of your light like dew.

Invocation from the Northumbrian Office, Celtic Night Prayer
© Northumbria Community Trust

90 Lord Of The Heavens And The Earth

Lucy Fisher

Lord of the hea - vens and the earth, my Sa - viour, Re- deem - er, ris - en Lord.

All ho- nour and glo - ry, power and strength to him up- on the throne.

Ho- ly, ho - ly, you are wor - thy,
Glo- ry, glo - ry, al - le - lu - ia,

91 Lord, You Have My Heart

Martin Smith

Tenderly ♩ = 110

Lord, you have— my heart,— and I will search— for yours:—

Je - sus, take— my life— and lead me
let me be— to you— a sac - ri -

on.
- fice.

(MEN) And

(WOMEN) I will praise you,—

I will praise you,— Lord, and

217

92 Love Songs From Heaven
(In This Dark World A Light Will Shine)

With strength ♩ = 84

Noel & Tricia Richards

1. Love songs— from hea - ven— are fil - ling— the earth,
2. No - thing has si - lenced— this gos - pel— of Christ;
3. Let ev - ery na - tion— be filled with— your song;

bring - ing— great hope to— all na - tions;
it ech - oes down through— the a - ges.
this is— the cry of— your peo - ple,

e - vil— has pros - pered,— but truth is— a - live -
Blood of— the mar - tyrs— has made your— church strong -
'we will— not set - tle— for a - ny - thing less -

in this— dark world the light still shines.
in this— dark world the light still shines.
in this— dark world, our light must shine.'

This song is recorded on the Spring Harvest 1997 Live Worship Album - Volume 1.

For you we live, and for you we may die, through us may Jesus be seen; for you alone we will offer our lives in this dark world, our light will shine.

92a Greeting each other
from Galatians 1

Grace and peace to you from
God our Father and the Lord Jesus Christ:
to God be glory for ever and ever! Amen.

93 More Than Oxygen

Brian Doerksen

1. More than ox - y - gen,— I need your love,—
2. More than mag-net and steel— are drawn to u - nite,—

more than life- giv- ing food— the hun- gry dream of;
more than po - ets love words— to rhyme as they write;-

more than an el - o- quent word—
more than the com - fort- ing warmth.

This song is recorded on the Spring Harvest 1997 New Songs Album, 1997 Praise Mix and 1997 Live Worship - Vol. 2.

more than the tall e-ver greens___ reach for_ the light;

more than the pound-ing waves_____ long for_ the_

_ shore,___ more than these gifts_ you give,_

_ I love_ you___ more._ More than_ a

93a Evangelism
from Colossians 4: 5-6

Be wise in the way you act towards outsiders; make the most of every opportunity. Let your conversations be always full of grace, seasoned with salt, so that you may know how to answer everyone.

94 Men Of Faith

♩ = 100

Martin Smith

1. Men of faith, rise up and sing of the great and glor-ious
(2) wo-men of the truth, stand and sing to bro-ken
(3) church with bro-ken wings; fill this place with songs a-

King; you are strong when you feel weak, in your bro-ken-ness com-
hearts, who can know the heal-ing power of our glor-ious King of
gain, of our God who reigns on high: by his grace a-gain we'll

plete.
love.
fly.

Shout to the

north and the south, sing to the east and the west:

'Je - sus is sa- viour to all, Lord of hea- ven and

earth.' _____

2. Rise up
3. Rise up

We've been through fire, — we've been through rain; we've been re-fined by the

power of his name. We've fal-len deep-er in love with you,

you've burned the truth on our lips. _____

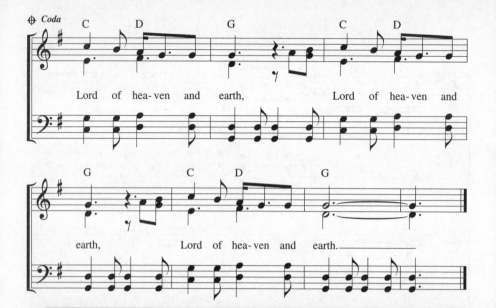

⊕ Coda

Lord of hea-ven and earth, Lord of hea-ven and

earth, Lord of hea-ven and earth.

94a   Life in the world

from Psalm 115, Gen 18, Eph 4, Prov 22, Micah 6, Jer 29, Rom 8, Col 1

The heavens are the Lord's;
the earth he has entrusted to the children of Adam.

God is the Judge of all the earth;
he has made us members one of another.

Rich and poor meet in this;
the Lord is the maker of them all.

What does the Lord require of us?
To act justly, to love mercy, and to walk humbly with our God.

Seek the welfare of the city to which he sends you,
and pray to the Lord on its behalf;
for in its welfare we will find our welfare.

The creation has been subject to decay;
it waits with eager longing for the revealing of the children of God.

The whole creation groans in the pains of labour until now;
we ourselves groan inwardly as we wait for the redemption of our bodies.

It is Christ we proclaim, the hope of glory;
bearing in our flesh the completion of his sufferings.

Whatever you do, in word or deed,
do everything in the name of the Lord Jesus,
giving thanks to God the Father through him.

© Michael Vasey

95 My Friend And King

Gently

James Taylor

1. My friend and King, love sweet-er than a rose, you meet me where I am. What can I do but bow
2. To be with you is all that I de-sire; Lord, may you shine in me. You gave me life and sa-

228

96 My First Love
(Like A Child)

As a jig

Stuart Townend

1. My first— love is a blaz- ing fi - re, I feel his power-ful—
2. My first— love is a rush- ing riv - er, a wa- ter - fall that will
3. Re- store the years of the chur- ch's slum ber, re- vive the fire that has

love in me; for he has kin- dled a flame of pas - sion,
nev - er cease; and in the tor- rent of tears and laugh- ter,
grown so dim; re- new the love of those first en- coun- ters,

and I will let it grow in me. And in the night I will
I feel a heal- ing power re- leased. And I will draw from your
that we may come a - live a - gain. And we will rise like the

sing your praise, my love.———
well of life, my love,———
dawn through - out the earth,———

And in the morn-ing I'll seek your face, my love.
and in your grace I'll be sa - tis - fied, my love.
un - til the trum-pet an - noun-ces your re - turn.

And like a child I will dance in your pres-ence,

O, let the joy of hea-ven pour down on me. I still re-mem-ber the

first day I met you, and I don't ev-er want to lose that fire, my first

love.

97 My Heart Is Full
(All the Glory)

From Hebrews 1
Graham Kendrick

Moderate ♩ = 65

1. My heart is full of ad-mi-ra-tion for you, my Lord, my God and King; your ex-cel-lence my in-spi-ra-tion, your words of grace have made my spi-rit sing. 2. You love what's

Je - sus, Sav - iour, a - noint - ed One, I wor - ship you, I wor - ship you; I wor - ship you, I wor - ship you.

97a   Responsive Covenant

I am no longer my own, but yours.
Put me to what you will,
rank me with whom you will.
Put me to doing, put me to suffering.
Let me be employed for you, or laid aside for you;
exalted for you, or brought low for you.
Let me be full, let me be empty;
let me have all things, let me have nothing.
I freely and gladly yield all things
to your pleasure and disposal.
And now, O glorious and blessed God,
Father, Son and Holy Spirit,
you are mine and I am yours. So be it.
And the Covenant which I have made on earth,
let it be ratified in heaven.
Amen.

© Taken from the Covenant Service Methodist Book of Offices.

98 My Jesus I Love Thee

R. Featherstone
Music: Adoniram J. Gordon

♩ = 100

Je - sus I love thee, I know thou art
(2) love thee be - cause thou has first loved
(3) man - sions of glo - ry an end - less de -

mine; for thee, all the fol - lies of
me and pur - chased my par - don on
light, I'll ev - er a - dore thee in

sin I re - sign. My gra - cious Re -
Cal - va - ry's tree. I love thee for
hea - ven so bright. I'll sing with the

236

deem - er, my Sav - iour art thou,——— if
wear - ing the thorns—— on thy brow -—— if
glit - ter - ing crown—— on my brow,——— 'if

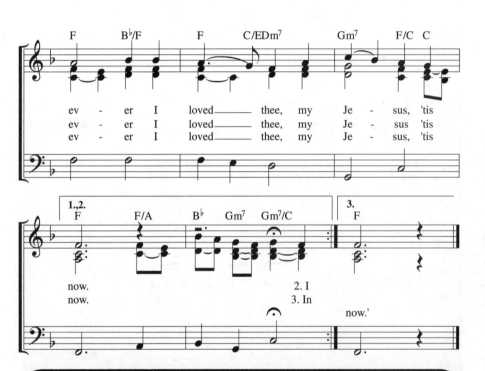

ev - er I loved——— thee, my Je - sus, 'tis
ev - er I loved——— thee, my Je - sus 'tis
ev - er I loved——— thee, my Je - sus, 'tis

now.
now.
                    2. I
                    3. In
                        now.'

98a   The Eucharistic prayer

The Lord is here.
His Spirit is with us.

Lift up your hearts.
We lift them to the Lord.

Let us give thanks to the Lord our God.
It is right to give him thanks and praise.

99 My Jesus, My Lifeline

Tim Hughes

This song is recorded on the Spring Harvest 1998 r:age Album and the 1998 Praise Mix.

O Je-sus, sweet Je-sus,— ac-cept— this— love I give to you,— it's all I can do.—

99a　Thanksgiving for our families

Let us thank God for giving other people to be part of our lives

For parents, and the love which brought us to birth
we praise you, Lord, **and bring you thanks today.**

For brothers and sisters with whom we have shared our lives
we praise you, Lord, **and bring you thanks today.**

For all family and friends who have been with us in our sorrows
and our joys we praise you, Lord, **and bring you thanks today.**

For those who pointed us to Jesus, and who drew us into the family
of the church we praise you, Lord, **and bring you thanks today.**

**Help us to live
as those who follow you together
and belong to one another
now and always. Amen.**

100 My Jesus, My Saviour
(Shout To The Lord)

Darlene Zschech

My Je-sus, my Sa-viour, Lord, there is none— like— you;— all of my days— I want to praise— the won-ders of your migh-ty love. My com-fort, my shel-ter, tow-er of re-fuge and strength,— let ev-ery breath,— all that I am,— ne-ver cease to wor-ship you. Shout to the Lord— all the earth—

This song is recorded on the Spring Harvest 1996 Live Worship Album - Volume 1 and 1996 New Songs Album.

101 My Song Is Love Unknown

Words: Samuel Crossman
in this version Jubilate Hymns
Music: John Ireland
Arr. Chris Norton

1. My song is love un - known, my Sa - viour's love for
2. He came from hea - ven's throne sal - va - tion to be -
3. Some - times they crowd his way and his sweet prai - ses
4. Why, what has my Lord done to cause this rage and
5. With an - gry shouts, they have my dear Lord done a -
6. In life no house, no home, my Lord on earth may
7. Here might I stay and sing of him my soul a -

me; love to the love - less shown that they might
stow; but men re - fused, and none the longed - for
sing, re - sound - ing all the day ho - san - nas
spite? He made the lame to run, and gave the
way; a mur - der - er they save, the Prince of
have; in death no friend - ly tomb but what a
dores; ne - ver was love, dear King, ne - ver was

Bridges — From F

To B♭

To C

To D

To E♭

To G

102 No Scenes Of Stately Majesty

scenes of state - ly ma - jes - ty for — the — King of
wreaths up - on the ground were laid for — the — King of
na - ture's fin - est co - lours blaze for — the — King of
prayers shall be a fra - grance sweet for — the — King of
long for scenes of ma - jes - ty for — the — ris - en

kings; no nights a - glow with can - dle flame___
kings; on - ly a crown of thorns re - mained___
kings; and stars in jew - elled clus - ters say___
kings; my love, the flow - ers at his feet___
King, for nights a - glow with can - dle flame___

248

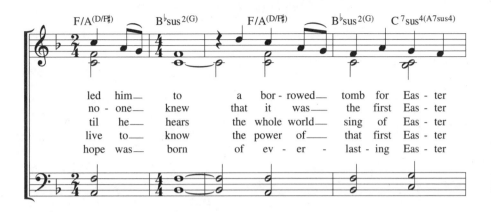

led him— to a bor - rowed— tomb for Eas - ter
no - one— knew that it was— the first Eas - ter
til he— hears the whole world— sing of Eas - ter
live to— know the power of— that first Eas - ter
hope was— born of ev - er - last - ing Eas - ter

Day.
Day.
love.
Day.
Day.

2. No
3. Yet
4. My
5. I

102a Lord of all life

from Colossians

Christ is the image of the invisible God,
the firstborn over all creation.
All things were made through him and for him;
in him all things hold together.

In him the fullness of God was pleased to dwell
and through him to reconcile all things on earth and in heaven,
making peace by the blood of his cross.

Whatever you do, in word or deed,
do everything in the name of the Lord Jesus,
giving thanks to God the Father through him.

Whatever your task, put your heart into it, as serving the Lord,
knowing that from him you will receive your inheritance.
We are serving Christ.

© Michael Vasey

103   No Song On Earth

Phil Baggaley
from *City of Gold*

Slowly ♩=82

1. No song on earth will ev - er sound like
   ci - ty on this earth will stand for
3. No king - dom knew of such a King, of

one be - fore your throne, when my - riads of the
all e - ter - ni - ty. The beau - ty of your
one so true and brave, who laid a - side his di -

an - gels sing in praise to you a - lone. No
pro - mised land, a wel - come there for me. Be -
- a - dem, for those he came to save. O

morn - ing sun,—— no har - vest moon— or
yond this noise—— to peace—— at last,— at
match - less love,—— such mer - cy free,— I

star can shine—— so bright;—— there's no-thing can— com-pare—
rest be - side— your throne,—— no ci - ty can— com-pare—
can-not com - pre - hend.—— There's no - one can— com-pare—

1st time D.S.
2nd time D.C.
3rd time Fine

—— with you,— my sweet e - ter - nal— light.—— 2. No
—— to this,— our sweet, e - ter - nal— home.——
—— to thee,— my Mas - ter and— my— friend.——

103a Into a desert place

Lord,
let our memory provide no shelter for grievance against
another.
Lord,
let our heart provide no harbour for hatred of another.
Lord,
let our tongue be no accomplice in the judgement of a
brother.

Into a desert place, the Cuthbert liturgy from the Northumbrian Office, Celtic Night Prayer
© Northumbria Community Trust

104 O Lord, Hear
(Breathe On Us Again)

Slowly

Steve Fry

O Lord, hear, O Lord, for-give us, we have
lost the awe of you, have mer-cy, have mer-cy.
O Lord, cleanse our hearts which are di-vid-ed; stir the
faith that we once knew, we're thirst-y, we're thirst-y.

253

105 O Adoramus Te Domine
(We Adore You, Lord Jesus Christ)

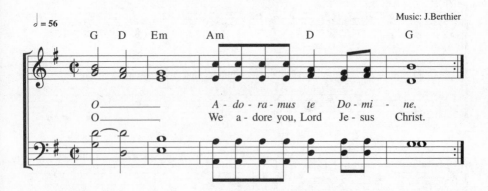

This song is recorded on the Spring Harvest 1997 Live Worship Album - Volume 2.

105a Approach to God

We have come to worship God our Father; to acknowledge his power and authority, to give thanks for his care and keeping, and to offer ourselves in the service of Christ:

He is the Creator:
he gives us life and breath.

He is Preserver of all life:
he sustains us day by day.

He is Redeemer of his people:
he shows us his love in Christ.

He is Lord of lords:
he controls all things.

**O God our Father,
we bring you our love and praise
and give you thanks
        for all your goodness,
through Jesus Christ our Lord. Amen.**

© CFW

106 O Your Hands Of Kindness
(Hands Of Kindness)

Slowly

Martin Smith

1. O, your hands of kind-ness___ are here___ for me,_
2. O, your hands of mer-cy___ were scarred_ for me,_
3. O, your love that burns me,___ deep-er than the sea,_

___ and I've heard they are silk-en___ and can car-ry me._
___ and your bo-dy was bro-ken___ so that I___ go free._
___ and the trea-sure I find here:_ the Sa-viour's love for me._

Chorus

___ How I love___ you, all I am is

you, King of love I bow.

D.C. **To end** D

107 Only By Grace

Gerrit Gufstafson

Only by grace can we en - ter, only by grace we can stand: not by our hu - man en-dea - vour, but by the blood of the Lamb. Into your pre - sence you call us, you call us to come. Into your pre - sence you draw us, and

now by your grace— we come,—   now by your grace— we come.—

Lord, if you mark— our trans-gres-

_ sions, who would stand?

Thanks to your grace— we are cleansed— by the blood— of the Lamb.—

108 Our Confidence Is In The Lord

Noel & Tricia Richards

Our con-fi-dence— is in the Lord,— the source of our— sal - va - tion.— Rest is found— in him a-lone,— the au - thor of— cre - a - tion.— We will not fear the ev - il day— be-cause we have a ref- uge; in ev-ery cir - cum-stance— we say,—

'Our hope is built on Je - sus.' He is our fort-ress, we will
nev-er be sha - ken;— he is our fort-ress, we will nev-er be shak - en.—
We will put our— trust— in— God;
we will put our— trust— in— God.
Our God.

109 Our God Is Great

Bright and rhythmic

Dave Bilbrough

flow - ers— that grow, morn - ing— and eve - ning,
soft fal - ling rain, the mist on— the hills, the

win - ter— and spring; come join all— cre - a - tion— and
light and— the shade; come join all— cre - a - tion— in

sing. Our God is For
praise.

mu - sic— and dan - cing,— the sounds that— we hear; for co-lours— and words, the

life that— we share,— we say: Our God is

110 Overwhelmed By Love

With feeling ♩ = 80

Noel Richards

O - ver - whelmed by love, deep-er than
All my sin was laid on your dear

o-ceans, high as the heav-ens; ev - er - liv-ing
Son, your pre-cious one;— all my debt he

God - your love has res-cued me.
paid, - great is your love for me.

2. No- one could ev - er earn your love;

This song is recorded on the Spring Harvest 1995 Live Worship Album.

110a   Tell it Among the Nations
from 1 Chronicles 16

O worship the Lord in the beauty of holiness,
let the whole earth stand in awe of him.

Tell it out among the nations that the Lord is King,
O worship the Lord in the beauty of holiness.

God's salvation has been openly shown to all people.
let the whole earth stand in awe of him.

Declare his glory among the nations and his wonders
among all peoples.
O worship the Lord in the beauty of holiness,
let the whole earth stand in awe of him.

111 Praise Be To Christ

Words: Timothy Dudley-Smith
Music: C Hubert Parry
Arr. Christopher Norton

Broadly ♩ = 94

1. Praise be to

Christ— in whom we— see the im-age of the Fa-ther
(2) him— whose sov-er-eign sway and will up-holds cre-a-tion's
(3) him— who, Lord most— high, the full-ness of the God-head

shown, the first-born Son re-vealed and known, the truth and
plan; who is, be-fore all worlds be-gan and when our
shares; and yet our hu-man na-ture bears, who came as

grace of de-i-ty; through whom cre-a-tion came to
world has passed a-way: Lord of the church, its life and
man to bleed and die: and from his cross there flows our

birth, whose fin - gers set the stars in place, the un - seen
head, re - demp-tion's price and source and theme, a - live, the
peace who chose for us the path he trod, that so might

powers, and this— small earth, the fur-thest bounds of time and
first - born from— the dead, to reign as all - in - all su -
sins and sor - rows cease and all be re - con-ciled to

1.,2.

space.
preme.

2. Praise be to
3. Praise be to

3.

God.

112 Praise God From Whom All Blessings Flow

Andy Piercy & Dave Clifton
Arr. Alison Berry

112a World of work

from Colossians 3: 23-24

Whatever you do, work at it with all your heart, as working for the Lord, not for men, since you know that you will receive an inheritance from the Lord as a reward. It is the Lord Christ you are serving.

Where was I?

```
Spear —    You pierced my Lord's side
Soldier —  You held the shaft
           To test for life
           You tore his body
           Caused blood to flow
Nails —    You held his wrists
           Impaled his body
           On wood
Wood —     You stretched him wide
           Held him up
           To take the scorn
Voice —    You mocked
```

And where was I that day
Hiding in the crowd?
Did I hold the hammer?
Did I carry the cross?
Did I write the sign?
Or make the crown of thorns?
Did I hide my shame
In the mockery?

Tell me where was I?
Did I watch from a distance
Afraid to come close?
Did I make my excuses
And pretend that I did all that I could?
Did I cast my judgement
Cry crucify
Or in my silence
Did I wash my hands?

Wherever I was — I wasn't at your side

I want to cry out
To take a sword and set you free
To raise my voice
Against the crowd.
Yet I was too late
Too late to change
For my lot was cast
Before I realised the shame.

Willing or not — I was there.

© Andrew Marshall

113 Praise, My Soul

Words: from Psalm 103
Henry Francis Lyte
Music: John Goss
Arr. David Peacock

With strength ♩ = 102

1. Praise, my soul, the king of hea - ven; to his feet your tri - bute bring! Ran - somed, healed, re - stored, for - gi - ven,
2. Praise him for his grace and fa - vour to our fa - thers in dis - tress; praise him still the same as ev - er,
3. Fa - ther - like he tends and spares us; all our hopes and fears he knows, in his hands he gent - ly bears us,
4. An - gels, help us to a - dore him - you be - hold him face to face; sun and moon, bow down be - fore him -

This song is recorded on the Spring Harvest 1997 Live Worship Album - Volume 2.

who   like   me   his   praise should sing?   Al- le - lu - ia,
slow   to   blame and   swift   to   bless,   Al- le - lu - ia,
res - cues   us   from   all   our   foes,   Al- le - lu - ia,
praise   him,   all   in   time   and   space,   Al- le - lu - ia,

al - le - lu - ia!   praise the   ev - er - last - ing King!
al - le - lu - ia!   glo - rious   in   his   faith - ful - ness!
al - le - lu - ia!   wide - ly   as   his   mer - cy   flows.
al - le - lu - ia!   praise with   us   the

God   of   grace!

114   Praise To The Holiest
In The Highest

Words: John Newman
Music: John Dykes
Arr. Roger Mayor

1. Praise to the Hol - iest in the height,
and in the depth be praise; in all his
2. Oh lov - ing wis - dom of our God!
when all was sin and shame, a sec - ond
3. Oh wis - est love! that flesh and blood,
which did in A - dam fail, should strive a -
4. And that the high - est gift of grace
should flesh and blood re - fine: God's pre - sence
5. Oh gener - ous love! that he who came
as man to smite our foe, the dou - ble
6. And in the gar - den sec - ret - ly,
and on the cross on high, should teach his
7. Praise to the Hol - iest in the height,
and in the depth be praise; in all his

Music arrangement © Roger Mayor/ Jubilate Hymns
4 Thorne Park Road, Chelston, Torquay, TQ2 6RX.

Chords (top system): Am G/B G/C Am/C A/C# D Em Am/C Am

words   most   won - der - ful,   most   sure   in
A - dam   to___   the   fight   and   to   the
fresh   a - gainst___   the   foe,   should   strive   and
and   his   ve - ry   self,   and   es - sence
a - go - ny___   for   us   as   man   should
breth - ren,   and___   in - spire   to   suf - fer
words   most   won - der - ful,   most   sure   in

Chords (second system): G/D D7   1.-6. Gsus   G   D7sus4   7. Gsus   G

all   his   ways!
res - cue   came.
should   pre - vail.
all - di - vine.
un - der - go.
and   to   die.
all   his   ways!

114a   Declaration of faith

To whom shall we go?
You have the words of eternal life,
and we have believed and have come to know
that You are the Holy One of God.
Praise to You, Lord Jesus Christ, King of Endless glory.

Morning Prayer from the Northumbrian Office, Celtic Daily Prayer
© Northumbria Community Trust

115 Purify My Heart
(Refiner's Fire)

116 Rejoice, Rejoice
(Hope Of Glory)

Graham Kendrick

Triumphantly

Re - joice! Re-joice! Christ— is in you, the hope of glo-ry in—

— our— hearts. He lives! He lives! His breath— is in you, a-

rise a migh-ty ar-my,— we ar-rise._____

Fine

1. Now   is   the
2. God   is   at
3. Though we   are

time for us— to march up - on the land,— in - to our
work in us— his pur - pose to per- form,— build - ing a
weak, his grace— is ev - ery- thing we need;— we're made of

hands he will give the ground— we claim.——
king - dom of pow - er not— of words,——
clay but this trea - sure is— with - in.——

He rides in ma - jes- ty— to lead us in - to
where things im - pos - si- ble— by faith shall be made
He turns our weak - nes-ses— in - to his op - por -

vic - to - ry,— the world shall see that Christ is Lord!——
pos - si - ble;— let's give the glo- ry to him now.—— Re -
tu - ni- ties,— so that the glo- ry goes to him.——

117 Righteous And Holy
(Honour And Praise)

With motion

Twila Paris

Right-eous and ho-ly in all of your ways,
Fill-ing the tem-ple, the work of your grace,
we come be-fore you with hon-our and praise. Here to a-dore you for all of our days, we come be-fore you with hon-our and praise.___ Lord of the hea-vens, how___ faith-ful you___

118 Say The Word

Steadily
Capo 1 (D)

Stuart Townend

1. Say the word, I will be healed; you are the great phy-si-cian, you meet ev-'ry need.__ Say the word, I will be free; where chains have held me cap-tive, come sing your songs to me. Say the

2. Say the word, I will be filled; my hands reach out to hea-ven where stri-ving is stilled.__ Say the word, I will be changed; where I am dry and thir-sty, send cool, re-fresh-ing rain. Say the

3. Say the word, I will be poor, that I might know the rich-es that you have in store.__ Say the word, I will be weak; your strength will be the pow-er that sa-tis-fies the meek. Say the

This song is recorded on the Spring Harvest 1998 New Songs Album.

282

118a Following God's Way

Will you continue in the apostles' teaching and fellowship,
in the breaking of bread, and in the prayers?
With the help of God, I will.

Will you persevere in resisting evil, and,
whenever you fall into sin, repent and return to the Lord?
With the help of God, I will.

Will you proclaim by word and example
the good news of God in Christ?
With the help of God, I will.

Will you seek and serve Christ in all people,
loving your neighbour as yourself?
With the help of God, I will.

Will you acknowledge Christ's authority over human society,
by prayer for the world and its leaders,
by defending the weak, and by seeking peace and justice?
With the help of God, I will.

ECUSA Bk of Common Prayer

119 Safe In The Shadow Of The Lord

Words: from Psalm 9
Timothy Dudley-Smith
Music: Norman Warren
Arr. Roger Mayer

1. Safe in the sha - dow of the Lord, be -
2. My hope is set on God a - lone though
3. From fears and phan - toms of the night, from
4. His ho - ly an - gels keep my feet se -
5. Strong in the ev - er - last - ing name, and
6. Safe in the sha - dow of the Lord, pos -

neath his hand____ and power,_____ I
Sa - tan spreads____ his snare;_____ I
foes a - bout____ my way,_____ I
cure from ev - ery stone;_____ I
in my Fa - ther's care,_____ I
sessed by love____ di - ine,_____ I

120 Salvation Belongs To Our God

Adrian Howard
& Pat Turner

120a   Offertory Prayer

Heavenly Father,
let these gifts go where we cannot go,
and help those whom we cannot reach;
through them
let the unlearned be taught,
the hungry fed,
the sick healed
and the lost found;
for Jesus' sake. Amen.

121 Sound The Trumpet

Dave Bilbrough

Strong and rhythmic

Sound the trum- pet, strike the drum, see the King of glo- ry come,
join the prai- ses ris - ing from the peo - ple of the Lord.
Let your voic- es now be heard, un - re- strained and un - re- served. Pre -
pare the way— for his re- turn,— you peo- ple of the Lord. Sing, 'Je- sus is

122 Spirit Of The Living God
(Break Me, Melt Me, Mould Me)

Daniel Iverson
Arr. W.G.Hathaway

123   Such Love

1. Such love, pure as the whit-est snow,
   such love, weeps for the shame I know,
   such love, pay-ing the debt I owe—
   O Je-sus, such love!

2. Such love, still-ing my rest-less-ness,
   such love, fill-ing my emp-ti-ness,
   such love, show-ing me ho-li-ness—
   O Je-sus, such love!

3. Such love springs from e-ter-ni-ty,
   such love, stream-ing through his-to-ry,
   such love, foun-tain of life to me—
   O Je-sus, such love!

124 Tell The World

Dave Bilbrough

Chorus

Tell the world that Je-sus is ris-en, let his praise en-cir-cle the globe; make it known a-mong all the na-tions that Je-sus is a-live!

Last time to Coda

(v2.)

Verse

1. From the cra-dle to the grave, from a sta-ble to a cross;
2. No eye has seen, no ear has heard what he's pre-pared;

This song is recorded on the Spring Harvest 1998 New Songs Album.

his life was of-fered up in sac-ri-fice___ for us.
his re-su-rec-tion means his life is ours___ to share.

He came from hea-ven's throne to seek and save the lost;___ to
The great-est mi-ra-cle of all has tak-en place;___

re-con-cile us back to God.___
Christ has ris-en - he is Lord.___

Coda

125 Thank You For Saving Me

With a steady rhythm ♩ = 100

Martin Smith

1. Thank you for saving me; what can I say?
2. Mercy and grace are mine, forgiven is my sin-

You are my everything, I will sing your praise.
Jesus, my only hope, the Saviour of the world.

You shed your blood for me - what can I say?
'Great is the Lord,' we cry, 'God, let your kingdom come!'

You took my sin and shame, a sinner called by name.
Your word has let me see, thank you for saving me.

This song is recorded on the Spring Harvest 1994 Live Worship Album.

126 The Father's Heart Is Breaking

♩ = 120   Geoff Baker

1. The Fa - ther's heart is break - ing, there's
2. Lord, fill me with a pas - sion, your
3. I want to speed the com - ing of that

dark - ness in the land. His child - ren are for -
fi - re from a - bove; a hea - ven - ly com -
great and glo - rious day; to see an end of

sak - ing the work that he has planned. The
pas - sion to reach this world you love; a
suf - fer - ing, our te - ars wiped a - way; to

world is slip - ping si - lent - ly in - to a lost e -
heart that weeps the Fa - ther's tears, a love that con - quers
stand be - fore my migh - ty King, how - ev - er weak my

ter - ni - ty,——— will no - one tell——— them of the Sa - viour's
all my fears,——— a vi - sion that——— can see the path——— you
of - fer - ing,——— and know that it——— was in my heart——— to

Chorus

love?——————— I'm here—— Lord, I'm here——Lord, I'm pre -
show.———————
say:———————

pared to take—— a stand. I'll go—— Lord, I'll go—— Lord, I will

fol - low your—— com - mand. Though I am weak—— and fear - ful, I

hum - bly bow— the knee,_____ in faith— Lord, in

faith— Lord, cry-ing here am I,_____ send—— me._____

126a Morning Prayer

One thing I have asked of the Lord,
this is what I seek:
that I may dwell in the house of the Lord
all the days of my life;
to behold the beauty of the Lord
and to seek Him in His temple.

Call: Who is it that you seek?
Response: **We seek the Lord our God.**

Call: Do you seek Him with all your heart?
Response: **Amen. Lord, have mercy.**

Call: Do you seek Him with all your soul?
Response: **Amen. Lord, have mercy.**

Call: Do you seek Him with all your mind?
Response: **Amen. Lord, have mercy.**

Call: Do you seek Him with all your strength?
Response: **Amen. Christ, have mercy.**

Morning Prayer from the Northumbrian Office, Celtic Daily Prayer
© Northumbria Community Trust

127 The Spirit Of The Sov'reign Lord (*Spirit Of The Sovereign Lord*)

Andy Park

1. The Spi-rit of— the sov'-reign Lord is up-on— you, be-cause he has— a-noint-ed you to preach good— news.— 1. The
2. The Spi-rit of— the sov'-reign Lord is up-on— us, be-cause he has— a-noint-ed us to preach good— news.— 2. The

news.— He has sent you to— the poor,— to bind up the bro-ken-heart-
news.— He will com-fort all— who mourn,— he will pro-vide for those— who grieve,-

(this is the year,—)

This song is recorded on the Spring Harvest 1998 New Songs Album.

ed, *(this is the day, —)* to bring free - dom to the cap -
he will pour out the oil of glad -

- tives, *(this is the year, —)* and to re - lease— the ones— in
- ness, in - stead of mourn - ing you— will

Chorus

dark - ness. This is— the year— of the fa - vour of the Lord,-
praise.—

— this is— the day— of the ven - geance of our God,-

this is— the year— of the fa - vour of the Lord,—

this is— the day— of the ven - geance of our God.—

To repeat F/G(D)

Last time F/G(D) *Fine* Gm(Em)

2. The

127a Prayer of Humble Access

We do not presume to come to your table,
merciful Lord, trusting in our own righteousness,
but in your manifold and great mercies.
We are not worthy so much as to
gather up the crumbs under your table.
But you are the same Lord
whose nature is always to have mercy.
Grant us therefore, gracious Lord,
so to eat the flesh of your dear Son Jesus Christ
and to drink his blood,
that we may evermore dwell in him
and he in us. **Amen.**

128 There Is A Name I Love To Hear

Words: F Whitfield
Music: W H Rudd

1. There is a name I love to hear, I
2. It tells me of a Saviour's love, who
3. It tells of one whose loving heart can
4. It bids my trembling heart rejoice, it
5. Jesus, the name I love so well, the

love to speak its worth; it sounds like music
died to set me free; it tells me of his
feel my deepest woe, who in my sorrow
dries each rising tear; it tells me in a
name I love to hear! No saints on earth its

in my ear, the sweetest name on earth.
precious blood, the sinner's perfect plea.
bears a part that none can bear below.
'still, small voice' to trust and never fear.
worth can tell, no heart conceive how dear.

O how I love the Sav - iour's name,
O how I
How I love— the Sav - iour's name,— how I

love the Sav - iour's name,
O how I love the
love— the Sav - iour's name, how I love, I love— the

Sav - iour's name,
the sweet - est name— on earth.
Sav - iour's name,

128a   False teaching
from Colossians 2: 8

See to it that no-one takes you captive through hollow and
deceptive philosophy, which depends on human tradition
and the basic principles of this world rather than on Christ.

129 There Is Power In The Name Of Jesus

Noel Richards

1. There is power in the name of Je - sus -
(2) power in the name of Je - sus,

we be - lieve in his name.
like a sword in our hands.

We have called on the name of Je - sus:
We de - clare in the name of Je - sus:

305

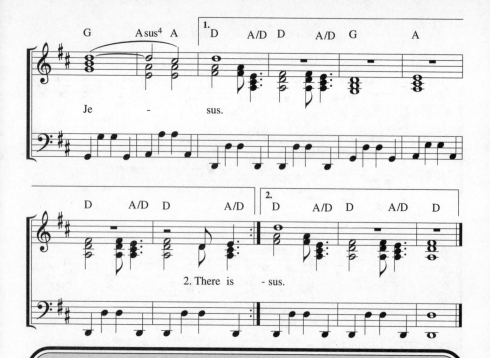

129a Praising God

The congregation may divide into two groups, A and B

Leader   Praise God, King of the Universe, who has
            created all things, and made humankind in his image.

A   Praise God, who has created courtship and marriage,
B   joy and gladness,
A   feasting and laughter,
B   pleasure and delight,
A   love, peace and fellowship.

B   Praise God, who has sent Jesus Christ
A   to save us from sin
B   to redeem our love from selfishness.

A   Praise God who has given us the Holy Spirit
B   to make us one with each other
A   to make us one with God.

All   **Praise God, King of the universe,
        who loved us into being
        and calls us to love one another. Amen.**

© Mark Earey, adapted from The Methodist Service Book 1975
(Methodist Publishing House, 1975). © Methodist Conference Office 1975.

130 There's A Place
(Because Of You)

Strong and rhythmic

Paul Oakley

1. There's a place where the streets shine with the
glo-ry of the Lamb. There's a
way we can go there, we can
live there be-yond time. Be-cause of you,

(2.) pain, no more sad-ness, no more
suffer-ing, no more tears, no more
sin, no more sick-ness, no in

3. There is joy ev-er-last-ing, there is
glad-ness, there is peace, there is
wine ev-er-flow-ing, there's a

To next section

131 These Are The Days Of Elijah
(Days Of Elijah)

Robin Mark

♩ = 103

1. These are the days of Elijah, declaring the word of the Lord; and these are the days of your servant, Moses, right-eous-ness be-ing re-stored. And though these are days of great tri-al, of fam-ine and dark-ness and sword, still

2. These are the days of Ezekiel, the dry bones be-com-ing as flesh; and these are the days of your servant, David, re-build-ing the tem-ple of praise. These are the days of the har-vest, the fields are as white in the world, and

This song is recorded on the Spring Harvest 1997 New Songs Album and 1997 Live Worship Album - Volume 1.

132 This Is The Place
(Holy Ground)

Dave Bilbrough

Steadily

1. This is the place where dreams are found;
   where vision comes called
   ho - ly ground.
   Holy ground,
   I'm stand-ing on holy ground for the

2. Your fi - re burns but nev - er dies;
   I re - al - ise this is
   ho - ly ground.

3. The great I Am re - vealed to man,
   take off your shoes, this is
   ho - ly ground.

Chorus

This song is recorded on the Spring Harvest 1998 r:age Album.

Lord my God is here with me.

Last time
G

132a When Relationships Go Wrong
based on Ecclesiastes 3

There's a time
a time for everything
a time to grieve
a time to be sad
a time to hurt
a time to cry
but listen child
this is not your time.
Let go of what has gone before
look to the new thing
that I am creating.

For this is your time
a time to walk again
a time to be healed
a time for new beginnings
a time to laugh
- to drive the sorrow from your soul.
A time to go forward
a time to be loved
a time to be who I created you to be
a time to wait
wait upon my timing.

So listen child, and listen well
this is your time and I long to fulfil.

© Andrew Marshall

133 This Is The Sweetest Mystery

Andy Piercy
& Dave Clifton

Meditatively ♩ = 100

1. This is the sweet-est mys-te-ry,— that you, O Lord are one— in three;— ma-jes-tic, glo-rious Tri-ni-ty— of Fa-ther, Spi-rit, Son;— the heaven - ly Fa-ther, great—

2. Lord, may this truth be-come a flame— that burns with-in our hearts— a-gain,— that we may glo-ri-fy your name— in all we do and say.— And so,— dear Lord,— we glad-

1st time D.C.
Last time to Coda

D.S. al Coda

Coda

Fine

Verse 1: I Am, the Son of God, the Son of Man, and yet with-in this won-drous plan: the Spi-rit with us here. And so, dear Lord, we glad-

Verse 2: -ly come to stand be-fore the Three in One, and wor-ship Fa-ther, Spi-rit, Son, ac-cept the praise we bring.

Ac-cept the praise we bring.

134 Through The Cross
(Healing River)

Steadily

Mike Burn

1. Through the cross,— Je-sus you tri-umphed, by your
(2) wounds— with-in our homes, Lord, re-con-
(3) walls— of i-so-la-tion, res-cue
(4) church— rise up as one now, join the

blood— you bought our peace. Where there
-cile— hus-bands and wives. Turn the
those— who live in fear. May the
streams— in one ac-cord. Young and

once was death and se-par-a-tion— your
fa-thers' hearts to-wards their child-ren,— O,
lone-ly find love in your fam-ily,— O,
old will stand and sing with one voice— to

heal - ing ri - ver flows.
let the ri - ver flow.
let the ri - ver flow.
praise our ri - sen Lord.

Let it flow, let it

flow, let the heal - ing ri - ver flow. Gra - cious

God_____ we cry to you: let the heal - ing ri - ver

flow._____

2. Bind up
3. Break down
4. May your

317

135 Time And Again

Caroline Bonnett,
Sue Rinaldi
& Steve Bassett

This song is recorded on the Spring Harvest 1998 New Songs Album.

136 To Be In Your Presence
(My Desire)

Noel Richards
Arr. L. Evans

To be in your pres-ence, to sit at your
To rest in your pres-ence, not rush-ing a-

feet,___ where your love sur-rounds me,
-way,___ to cher-ish each mo-ment-

and makes me com-plete:___ This is my___ de-
here I would stay:___

-sire, O___ Lord, this is my___ de-sire;

this is my— de - sire, O— Lord, this is my— de-

-sire.

136a   Gathering as God's Family

We have gathered here in the name of Jesus.
He is Lord!

We have come in the name of God the Father.
We are his children!

We have come in the name of the Holy Spirit.
He gives us life!

So why are we here?
**We have come together as the family of God,
in our Father's presence,
to offer him praise and thanksgiving,
to hear and receive his holy word,
to bring before him the needs of the world,
to ask his forgiveness of our sins,
and to seek his grace,
that through his Son Jesus Christ
we may give ourselves to his service.**

May God who has given us this desire, strengthen us in it.
Amen.

137 To You, O Lord

Graham Kendrick

Moderately

1. To you, O Lord, I lift up my soul,—
2. Show me your ways and teach me your paths,—
3. Re - mem - ber, Lord, your mer - cy and love—

in you I trust, O my God.—
guide me in truth, lead me on;—
that e - ver flow from of old.—

Do not let me be put to shame,—
for you're my God, you are my Sa - viour,
Re - mem - ber not the sins of my youth—

nor let my e - ne - mies— tri - umph o - ver me.—
my hope is in— you— each mo - ment of the day.—

3rd time D.S.

or my re-bel-li-ous ways. Ac-cord-ing to your love, re-mem-ber me, ac-cord-ing to your love, for you are good, O Lord.

Bridges — From G

To B♭

To C

To D

To E♭

To F

138 Turn Our Hearts

Graham Kendrick

Turn our hearts, turn our hearts.

1. Turn our hearts to one an - oth - er,
2. Turn our hearts from pride and an - ger
3. Turn the hearts of gen - er - a - tions
4. As we all have been for - giv - en,

let your kind- ness show: where our words or deeds have wound.- ed,
to your ways of peace, for you died and shed your blood that
that we may be one: make us part- ners in the king - dom
so we must for - give; as we all have found ac - cep - tance,

Last time to Coda

let for - give - ness flow.
en - mi - ty may cease.
'til your work is done.
so let us re - ceive.

⊕ *Coda*

Turn___ our___ hearts, change___ our___

hearts, join___ our___ hearts,

turn___ our___ hearts.

138a Looking beyond our families

God of community,
whose call is more insistent than ties of family or blood;
may we so respect and love
those whose lives are linked with ours
that we fail not in loyalty to you,
but make choices according to your will,
through Jesus Christ. Amen.

© All Desires Known, Janet Morley (Movement for the Ordination of Women, 1988). © Janet Morley 1988

139 Unshakable, Immovable
(These Things Are True Of You)

Steadily

Tommy Walker

1. Un - shak - a - ble, im - mov - a - ble, faith - ful and true; full of wis - dom, strength and beau - ty:— these things are true of you. Fear - less, cour - a - geous, right - eous - ness shines through in all—

2. Pa - tient, com - pas - sion - ate, love flows through you; you nev - er give up on the hope - less ones:— these things are true of you. Ho - ly and blame - less, you stand up for just - ice—

140   We Bow Down

Viola Grafstrom

Gently, with awe

We bow down and con - fess you are Lord in this place.

We bow down and con - fess you are Lord in this place.

This song is recorded on the Spring Harvest 1998 New Songs Album.

141 We Must Work Together
(We'll See It All)

With strength

Ian Mizen
& Andy Pressdee

We must work to-geth - er, bring-ing in the king-dom, bring-ing
We will see the dawn - ing, in this ge-ne - ra - tion see the

heav-en here on earth. Start a new world or - der,
start of a new day. We'll know peace and free - dom,

start a re-vo-lu - tion, let all peo-ple know their worth.
we will know true laugh - ter, we'll see sick-ness blown a - way.

We'll see it all, (we'll see it all,———) we'll see it all,

This song is recorded on the Spring Harvest 1997 Live Worship Album - Volume 1.

142 We See Jesus

Colossians 2:16
David W Morris
& Mike Massa

We see Je - sus - for his suf-fering crowned with glo-ry and with
praise, tast - ing death for all men by God's grace,
giv-en power to put all things in place;_____ and we see
Je - sus - seat-ed at the right hand of the throne,
mak-ing in-ter-ces-sion for his own, up - hold-ing all things by his word a-

335

143 We Want To See Jesus Lifted High

Doug Horley

Lively ♩ = 160

We want to see Je - sus lift - ed high-— a ban-ner that flies-— — a-cross-— this land;-— that all men might see-— the truth-— and know-— — he is the way-— to heav - en. We want to see, (We're gon - na) we want to see, (we're gon-na) we want to see Je - sus lift - ed high.- (we're gon-na)

This song is recorded on the Spring Harvest 1994 Live Worship Album and the 1994 Praise Mix.

144 We Worship And Adore You

Andy Piercy
Words for v3: Cecil F. Alexander
Arr. Alison Berry

This song is recorded on the Spring Harvest 1996 New Songs Album.

145 We Want To Change This World *(Change This World)*

With a steady rhythm ♩ = 84

Sue Rinaldi

We want to change this world,—— we want to change this world.—— We want to

1. So wave those flags of jus-tice o-ver the na-tions,
2. So hold each oth-ers hands— a-cross the o-ceans,

and hit those drums of peace— a-mong—the
and play those chords of peace— a-mong—the

as we live out— ho - ly lives;— and

we want to change this world—— as you wash our— mo- tives clean.—

And — O, wash— us— clean!

145a Blessing

May the peace of the Lord Christ go with you,
wherever He may send you,
May He guide you through the wilderness,
protect you through the storm.
May He bring you home rejoicing
at the wonders He has shown you,
May He bring you home rejoicing
once again into our doors.

Morning Prayer from the Northumbrian Office, Celtic Daily Prayer
© Northumbria Community Trust

146 We've Got To See An End
(Waiting For The Healing)

Ian Mizen
& Andy Pressdee

Moderately

1. We've got to— see an end to the pain,—
your light to shine—

— the tears and— the— hurt - ing.
— and start a new— day.

How long— must we wait for you to
All your— pro - mis - es to take hold—

move— and bring an end to suf-fer - ing?
— and be come a re - a - li - ty?

This song is recorded on the Spring Harvest 1998 r:age Album and the 1998 Praise Mix.

er, your love will—show - er ov-er— us,

ov - er— us.— we're wait - ing— for the

146a   Come, Lord Jesus!
from the Book of Revelation

Let us say together in faith

Holy, holy, holy is the Lord God almighty,
who was, and is, and is to come.

We believe in God the Father,
who created all things
for by his will they were created and have their being.

We believe in God the Son,
who was slain
for with his blood, he purchased us for God,
from every tribe and language,
from every people and nation.

We believe in God the Holy Spirit
the Spirit and the Bride say, 'Come!'
Even so come, Lord Jesus!   Amen.

147 Well I've Got A Message To Bring *(Revival Town)*

Martin Smith
& Stuart Garrard

With a steady rhythm

- ry to tell___

1. Well, I've got a mes - sage to bring,___

a - bout the King a - bove___ all kings;___

I can't preach but I___ can___ sing,___

he spoke for peace, hope, love and jus - tice,

and me and my bro - thers here___

347

You may not hear it on the ra - di - o but__

'cause this is the free-dom gen-er - a - tion,____

G/A   Bm

you can feel it   on the air.

D/A   G

liv - ing   for re - viv - al in this   time.

Em   G   Bm

Hal - le - lu - jah,____   peo - ple

A   Em   G

ev - ery-where are sing - ing—   hal - le - lu - jah,____

148 We're Looking To Your Promise
(Send Revival)

Steadily

Matt Redman

Verse

C   F

1. We're look-ing to your pro-mise of old,— that if we pray—
   look-ing to the pro-mise you made,— that if we turn—

C   F

— and hum-ble our-selves,— you will— come—
— and look to your— face,— you will— come—

Am   F

— and heal our— land,— you will come,—
— and heal our— land,— you will come,—

C

1.
F

— you will come.—
— you will come—

2. We're

This song is recorded on the Spring Harvest 1998 Praise Mix.

149 What A Friend I've Found

Martin Smith

1. What a friend I've found, closer than a brother; I have felt your touch, more in-ti-mate than lov-ers. Je - sus, Je - sus, Je - sus, friend for e - ver.

2. What a hope I've found, more faith-ful than a mo-ther; it would break my heart to e-ver lose each oth-er.

This song is recorded on the Spring Harvest 1997 Live Worship Album - Volume 2.

150 When I Survey

Words: Issac Watts
Music adapted by E. Miller

1. When I_____ sur - vey the wond - rous cross on which the Prince of Glo - ry died,_____ my rich - est gain I count_____ as loss and pour con - tempt on all_____ my pride.

2. For - bid_____ it, Lord, that I should boast save in the cross of Christ_____ my God:_____ the ve - ry things that charm_____ me most - I sac - ri - fice them to_____ his blood.

3. See from_____ his head, his hands, his feet, sor - row and love flow ming - led down:_____ when did such love and sor - row meet or thorns com - pose so rich_____ a crown.

4. Were the_____ whole realm of na - ture mine, that were an of - fering far_____ too small;_____ love so a - maz - ing, so_____ di - vine, de - mands my soul, my life_____ my all!

151 When I Look To The Heavens
(Psalm 8)

Psalm 8
Trish Morgan
& Paula Simpson-Parry

1. When I look— to the hea-vens cre-a-ted— by your hands, I see the
(2) sing— to your name— to si-lence— all your foes; O Lord, your

moon— and the stars— that your fin-gers— set in place;— yet you
name— is so power-ful— too won-der-ful for words,— yet you

care for me—— with a love so— deep—— O—
care for me—— with a love so— deep—— O—

Lord,— you are— so great!— 2. Chil-dren
Lord,— you are— so great!—

This song is recorded on the Spring Harvest 1997 New Songs Album.

355

152 When I Walk Through The Waters
(Precious In Your Eyes)

Andy Piercy & Dave Clifton
Arr. Alison Berry

With a slow lilt ♩ = 80

1. When I walk through the wa- ters— I will not drown; when I walk through the fire— I shall not be burned for you have re- deemed—

152a Pressing on
from Colossians 4: 17

See to it that you complete the work you have received in
the Lord.

153   When The Music Fades
(Heart Of Worship)

Steadily
Capo 1 (D)

Matt Redman

1. When the mu - sic fades,_____ all is stripped a - way_____
2. King of end - less worth,_____ no one could ex - press_____

_____ and I sim - ply come,_____
_____ how much you de - serve._____

long - ing just to bring_____ some - thing that's of worth.
Though I'm weak and poor,_____ all I have is yours,

_____ that will bless your heart._____
_____ ev - ery sin - gle breath._____

This song is recorded on the Spring Harvest 1998 New Songs Album and the 1998 Praise Mix.

154 Where, O Death, Is Your Sting
(And Death Shall Have No Dominion)

Jonny Baker
& Jon Birch
Arr. R Spencer

1. Where, O death is your sting where is your vic-to-ry?
2. In the midst of strug-gl-ing re-call the me-mo-ry,
(3) dawn-ing of a new age, a new hu-man-i-ty:

Christ has plumbed the depths of hell and
Christ has tri-umphed ov-er death, the
re-demp-tion of cre-a-tion, Christ

walked out with the key. This hope in-spires
fi-nal e-ne-my.
is the gua-ran-tee.

me,

This song is recorded on the Spring Harvest 1998 r:age Album.

this hope in - spires_____ me.___

3. The

154a   Setting Our Hearts on God
from Colossians 3

'You have been raised with Christ.'
Lord, set our hearts on things above.

'Put to death all that belongs to your earthly nature
fornication, impurity, lust, evil desire and greed.'
Lord, set our hearts on things above.

'Rid your tongues of anger, rage, malice, slander,
lies and filthy language.'
Lord, set our hearts on things above.

'Clothe yourselves with compassion, kindness,
humility, gentleness and patience.'
Lord, set our hearts on things above.

'Bear with one another, and forgive as Christ forgave you.'
Lord, set our hearts on things above.

'Over all these virtues put on love,
which binds them together.'
Lord, set our hearts on things above.

**Clothe us with the new self renewed in the image of Christ
where Christ is all and in all and no divisions part us. Amen.**

© Mark Earey

155 Where Two Or Three

From Matthew 18
Graham Kendrick

Where two or three of you ga - ther in my name,

I am there, I am there with

you; and if just two of you stand in a -

gree - ment as you pray

156 Who Can Separate Us

David & Liz Morris

Who can sep - a - rate— us from the love— of God?—

— Who can sep - a - rate— us

from the love— of God?— Who can sep - a - rate—

— us from the love— of God?— That is in—

Je-sus— is Lord.——

Je-sus is Lord.——

156a God's 'foolish' wisdom

We praise you Jesus, for the way you came to us;
not as a ruler; but loving and serving us.
This is the stumbling block - Jesus our Lord!

We praise you Jesus, for the way you died for us;
you did no wrong; yet you died on the cross for us.
This is the stumbling block - Jesus our Lord!

We praise you Jesus, for crushing the pride in us;
we could not earn what you gave as a gift to us.
This is the stumbling block - Jesus our Lord!

We praise you Jesus, for showing God's plan to us;
foolish to many, God's wisdom walked here with us.
This is the stumbling block - Jesus our Lord!

© Mark Earey

157 Yes, Finished! The Messiah Dies

Words: Christopher Idle
Music: John Kelly
Arr. David Ball

1. Yes, fin - ished! The Mes - si - ah dies, cut off for sins, but not his own; com - plet - ed is the sa - cri - fice, the great re -

tem - ple cur - tain is torn down, the liv - ing way to heaven is seen; through Christ the mid - dle wall has gone, and all who

reign of sin and death is done, and all may live, from sin set free; Sa - tan and his pre - ten - ded throne are swal - lowed

Christ ac - cep - ted and brought near and clothed in right - eous - ness di - vine, I see the path to life made clear, and all your

deem - ing work is done.   Yes, fin - ished! All the debt is
will may en - ter in.   The an - cient sha - dows are ful -
up in vic - to - ry.   Saved from the curse of God I
me - rits, Lord, are mine.   Death, hell and sin are now sub -

paid,   jus - tice di - vine is sa - tis - fied,   the grand and
filled,   the Scrip- ture pro - phe- cies prove true,   the sin - less
am;   my Sav - iour hangs up - on a tree!   See there the
dued,   all grace is now to sin - ners given,   and so I

full a - tone - ment made; God for a guil - ty world has
Lamb of God is killed, the pro - mised co - ve - nant made
meek and si - lent Lamb; his fi - nal breath he breathes for
plead the a- ton - ing blood and claim the ti - tle deeds of

1.,2.,3.

died!
new!
me.

2. The
3. The
4. In

heaven.

158 You Are A Kind And Loving God
(You Care For Us)

Judy Bailey

1. You are a kind and lov - ing God:
2. Your ways are true, your ways are just,
3. Un - shak - en in your faith - ful - ness,

you keep us safe, watch ov - er us,
you dry our tears when times are tough,
you hear our prayers and ans - wer them,

you know our lives in ev - ery part
you're strong when we're not strong e - nough
you dis - ci - pline the ones you love

you care for us.
you care for us.
you care for us. You did not

This song is recorded on the Spring Harvest 1998 Praise Mix.

159 You Are My Passion

Noel & Tricia Richards
Arr. Caroline Bonnett

You are my pas-sion, love of my life -

friend and com-pan-ion - my lov-er.

All of my be-ing longs for your touch,

with all my heart I love you.

160   You Laid Aside Your Majesty

Noel Richards

You laid a - side your ma - jes - ty, gave up ev - ery - thing for me, suf - fered at the hands— of those you had cre - a - ted; you took all my guilt and shame, when you died— and rose a- gain-— now to - day— — you reign— in heaven and earth ex - alt - ed.

I real-ly want to wor-ship you, my Lord; you have won my
heart and I am yours for ev-er and ev-er: I will
love you. You are the on-ly one who died for me, gave your life
to set me free, so I lift my life to you in a-do-
ra- tion.

161 You're The Lion Of Judah
(Lion Of Judah)

Robin Mark

1. You're the Li-on of Ju-dah, the Lamb that was slain, you as-cend-ed to hea-ven and e-ver-more will reign; at the end of the age when the earth you re-claim, you will ga-ther the na-tions be-

2. There's a shield in our hand and a sword at our side, there's a fire in our spi-rit that can-not be de-nied; as the Fa-ther has told us, for these you have died, for the na-tions that ga-ther be-

162 Your Love, O Lord
(I Will Exalt You, O Lord)

Psalm 34
Peggy Caswell

1. Your love, O Lord, it reach-es to the hea- -vens; your faith-ful-ness, it reach- es to the skies; your

2. Your name, O Lord, it is a migh-ty tow- -er; your glo-ry - it cov- ers all the earth; your

right - eous - ness is like the migh - ty
in your hands a - lone are strength and

moun - tains how price - less is your faith - ful
pow - er all praise be to your glo - rious

love.
name.

I will ex -

alt you, O Lord,

I will ex - alt you, O Lord,

praise your ho-ly name that my heart may sing to you I will ex-alt you, O Lord.

1.

2. *Fine*

162a   Living as Families

God our Father,
your Son Jesus Christ lived in a family at Nazareth
grant that in our families on earth
we may so learn to love and to live together
that we may rejoice as one family in your heavenly
home;
through Jesus Christ our Lord. Amen.

© Church Family Worship (Hodder & Stoughton, 1986). © Jubilate Hymns Ltd. 1986
(No.193) from The Alternative Prayer Book 1984, Church of Ireland

163 Your Love Is Like An Eagle Soaring

Capo 3 (Bm)

Derek Bond

385

Guitar Chords

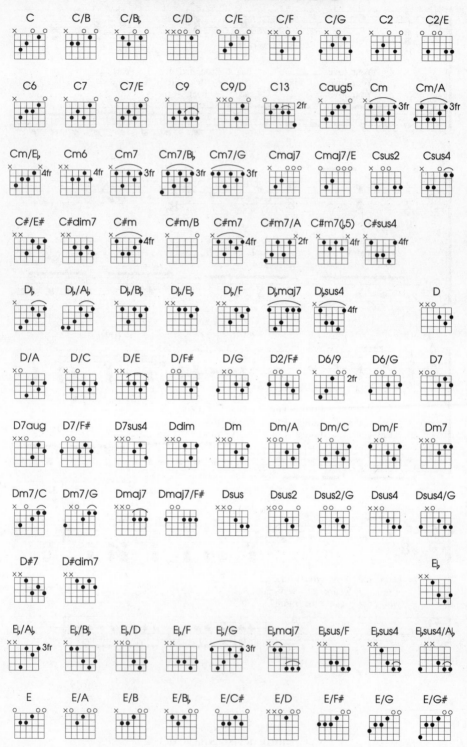

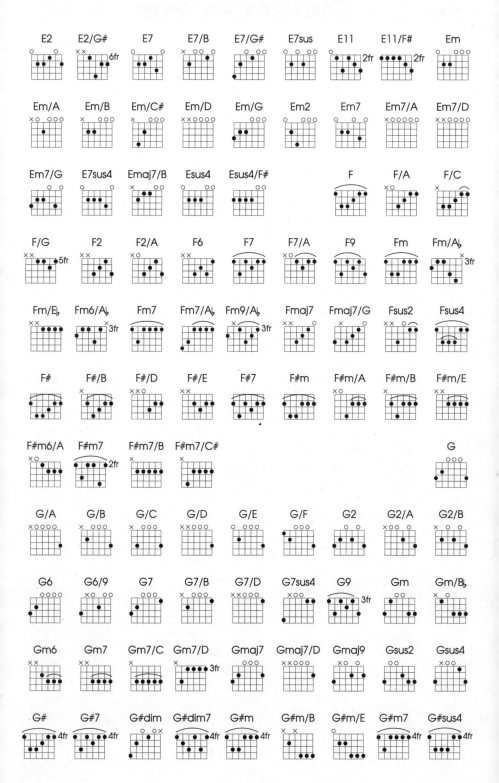

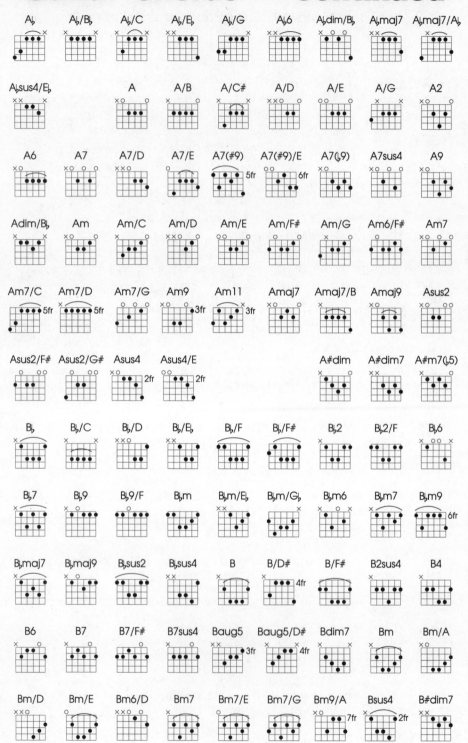

Thematic Index

The categories in this section are as follows:

Call To Worship   Holy Spirit
Church   Justice
Come, Lord Jesus   Love and Devotion
Confession   Mission
Cross   Praise and Thanksgiving
Dedication and Commitment   Prayer and Intercessions
Faith and Trust   Proclamation
Family Worship   Renewal and Refreshment
God, Lord and Father   Response
God, Mercy and Forgiveness   Spiritual Warfare
Healing   Suffering and Trials
Heart Worship

Thematic Index — continued

Come, Lord Jesus

Confession

Cross

Dedication & Commitment

Faith & Trust

Family Worship

God, Lord & Father

Thematic Index — continued

Holy Spirit

Justice

Love & Devotion

Thematic Index — continued

Prayer & Intercession

Proclamation

Renewal & Refreshment

Thematic Index — continued

Suffering & Trials

Worship Resources from Spring Harvest

Spring Harvest resources are available from your local Christian bookshop, or post-free direct from Spring Harvest. For credit card orders call our Customer Service team on 01825 769000.

BRAILLE & GIANT PRINT

Spring Harvest offer products for the partially sighted and the blind. The Spring Harvest words edition songbook is available in both giant print edition and a Braille version.

NEW SONGS 1998

Introducing some of the top new songs from this book - in a style that's carefully arranged and superbly produced. Songwriters include Dave Bilbrough, Chris Bowater, Matt Redman, Sue Rinaldi, Stuart Townend and Andy Park.

The arrangements are not too complex, so you can hear the melody and harmonies clearly. And if you lack musicians or instruments, there is a backing tracks cassette available.

CD ICCD 24330   CASSETTE ICC 24320   BACKING TRACKS CASSETTE ICC 24350

THE r:age ALBUM

Developing from the ground-breaking new styles in the 1997 Spring Harvest Praise Mix, this album includes ambient and hard core dance tracks amongst others. Many of the songs are taken from this book.

CD ICCD 24430   Cassette ICC 24420

PRAISE MIX 1998

Back to its roots in 1998, Praise Mix gives a contemporary feel to some of the newest worship songs. Dance and pop sounds give it genuine youth appeal.

CD ICCD 24530   Cassette ICC 24520

KIDS PRAISE and LITTLE KIDS PRAISE

Two new and lively collections of songs for children - specially recorded for Spring Harvest. Kid's Praise will appeal mainly to the 5 to 11 year old bracket. Little Kids Praise is a new product made to appeal to the under-fives - with backing tracks on side two of the cassette. The Kids Praise music book features all the songs from both these albums

Kids Praise CD ICCD 24630   cassette ICC 24620   Backing track cassette ICC 24650
Little Kids Praise cassette ICC 24720
Kids Praise & Little Kids Praise music book ICC 24610

SPRING HARVEST LIVE WORSHIP 1998

Available from June 1998 this album, recorded live during the Event, reflects the breadth of styles and range of worship leaders that make worship at Spring Harvest unique.

CD ICCD 25030   cassette ICC 25020

SPRING HARVEST

Equipping the Church for action

Spring Harvest — the Main Event

Every year, tens of thousands of Christians come to Spring Harvest's Eastertime Main Event. Alongside excellent Bible teaching, practical seminars, fun and fellowship you'll find superb worship in a whole variety of styles with leaders from varied church backgrounds.

For a free brochure, call
the Spring Harvest Customer Service team
on

01825 769000

or
use the Freepost card in the back of this book.

MUSIC AND WORSHIP RESOURCES FROM SPRING HARVEST

If you'd like to stay in touch with new resources from Spring Harvest, tear out this Freepost card and send us your details. Or simply call our Customer Service Team on 01825 769000. We'll make sure you are kept up to date.

Spring Harvest. A registered charity.

☐ Please keep me in touch with new resources from Spring Harvest

☐ Please send me a brochure about Spring Harvest - The Main Event

☐ Please send me details about help and discounts for group organisers

Name (Mr/Mrs/Ms)...

Address...

Postcode.................................Telephone.................................

MB98

21

Spring Harvest
Freepost (TN 6008)
14 Horsted Square
Uckfield
East Sussex
TN22 1BR